$4.95

69-2896

JEFFERSON COLLEGE

3 6021 00038 9241

WITHDRAWN

D1297191

WITHDRAWN

OK

PZ4   69-2896
.T93   Turing
My   My nephew Hamlet

Junior College District of
Jefferson County, Missouri
Library

WITHDRAWN

MY NEPHEW HAMLET

By the same author

MOVING HOUSE
NOTHING CERTAIN BUT TAX
101 POINTS ON BUYING A HOUSE

(*Hodder & Stoughton*)

MY NEPHEW
HAMLET

by

JOHN TURING

DRAWINGS BY
JILL McDONALD

LONDON
J. M. DENT & SONS LTD

A. S. BARNES & CO. INC.
SOUTH BRUNSWICK AND NEW YORK

Junior College District of
Jefferson County
Library

© John Turing, 1967
All rights reserved
Made in Great Britain
at the
Aldine Press · Letchworth · Herts
for
J. M. DENT & SONS LTD
Aldine House · Bedford Street · London
and
A. S. BARNES & CO. INC.
Cranbury, N.J. 08512
First published 1967

Library of Congress Catalog Card No. 68–10319

CONTENTS

To the memory of my brother Alan,
whose genius, having another bent, was slow to concede merit
in William Shakespeare's *magnum opus*
save for the final stage direction.

FOREWORD

The world of books is like life, in that you never know what you will encounter next. *My Nephew Hamlet* is an example of the surprising and the improbable. But it is a fact, and the reader must tackle it, to find out what kind of an animal it is, and if it can be given a class-name, as a matter of identity.

If it is a humorous ploy, it has something in common with the gentle but lethal mockery of Max Beerbohm. If it is intended as serious Shakespearean criticism, to add to the vast and ever growing body of Shakespeareana, then it bounces the lot. It is an original.

Nevertheless it purports to be a translation from the journal, written largely in early Danish, by King Claudius, the wicked uncle of Hamlet. Mr Turing explains all this elaborate machinery in his Preface. Or does he? Certainly he persuades the reader to go further, for he writes a prose which is most persuasive and graceful. He braces it with legal skill in argument, a technique which controls also the sinuosity with which King Claudius presents his case so convincingly.

By a magnificent disregard of the time element (the author has something to say about the tyranny of our general animus against the use of hindsight and anachronism) Claudius uses the very words of his later chronicler, William Shakespeare, as evidence in his own favour, to disprove the conclusions of the play and mankind's subsequent condemnation of the wicked murderer and usurper. Claudius proves that he is neither. By the cunning manipulation of evidence supplied by Shakespeare in the play, both in the verbal allusions and in the plot, here stands King Claudius, as clean as a whited sepulchre, and just as convincing.

That is not all. Hamlet, his mother, Polonius, and of course pretty little Ophelia, are all embraced within this new and most benevolent rearrangement of what happened in the draughty halls of Elsinore. Claudius stands as the one cornerstone (if that be possible in any structure) of the kingdom

threatened by the bellicose intentions of Norway. He does what
has to be done, and it is to be noted how smoothly he describes
the events that succeed his intentions. Mr Turing is almost
carried away as he transcribes, in a passage that rises to impres-
sive poetic beauty, the soliloquy in which Claudius repudiates
the very idea of being his brother's murderer. 'A brother's
murder! it has the primal eldest curse upon it!'

More than two opinions have always been held about the
character of Hamlet. The perennial argument, henceforth, is
likely to become more shrill, now that Claudius has had his
say; a plea so skilfully conveyed by Mr Turing.

RICHARD CHURCH

PREFACE

Here, presented for the first time and in an English translation, is a manuscript of rare literary and historic interest: none other than the journal of Claudius, uncle to the Prince of Denmark.

The familiar story of Claudius has been much bedevilled by the playwright Shakespeare, who corrupted the narrative of Kyd with such foreign matter as *The Murder of Gonzago*, of which Hamlet remarked: 'The story is extant and writ in very choice Italian.' Worse, Matthew Arnold laid a heavy hand on Shakespearean commentary ('Others abide our question. Thou art free'). Thus for long have scholars been encouraged to put Shakespeare beyond the bounds of wholesome criticism and to assume, contrary to reason and the evidence, that the great man never made mistakes, as the rest of us do, and that he always carefully checked and co-ordinated his plots and text. He didn't, of course; for one thing he was in the main concerned with the impact of the play on his audience, and for another he was far too busy, and we dare say he had no sooner written one play than his mind was filled to bursting with the next.

In a short essay on *Hamlet* Mr T. S. Eliot concluded that the play was almost certainly an artistic failure: 'Of all the plays it is the longest and is possibly the one on which Shakespeare spent most pains; yet he has left in it superfluous and inconsistent scenes which even hasty revision should have noticed.' In a telling phrase he described it as the 'Mona Lisa' of literature. Here is the genuine, uninhibited voice of literary appraisal, whether one agrees with it or not.

Mr J. M. Robertson made the point, cited with approval by Mr Eliot, that *Hamlet* 'is a stratification, that it represents the efforts of a series of men, each making what he could out of the work of his predecessors'. In another matter also they were of one mind, holding (as Mr Eliot put it) that 'the essential emotion of the play is the feeling of a son towards a guilty mother'—a proposition with which, as it happens, this editor wholly disagrees. But it remains true that the material proved too intractable to be manipulated into a cohesive and artistic whole. It is by its jewelled language, its emotional impact and its characterization that the play lives on.

This journal, written by the hand of Claudius himself, should correct many erratic notions rooted in Shakespeare's reconstruction of events. We are fortunately disembarrassed of the problem of 'stratification' for the very good reason that Claudius was a contemporary observer of events.

It is perhaps too much to hope that publication of the journal will for ever still the interminable agitations of the erudite, whose ingenuity of interpretation is matched only by their unbelievable capacity for raging furiously together. We believe that one who came nearer the mark than many of the pundits, before or since, was the old lady who was taken to see *Hamlet* for the first time and, according to legend, remarked afterwards that she found the plot obscure and there were far too many quotations. Though indeed, virtue herself 'scapes not calumnious strokes: Claudius, also, as appears from these pages, is not guiltless of too liberal borrowing of the choice phrase.

What was the play about? The implacable vengeance of the Ghost? The madness, or simulated madness, of Hamlet? The intolerable burden laid upon him which so nearly crushed his spirit? His procrastinations and vacillations? Are we to believe with William Richardson that 'the impropriety of Gertrude's behaviour, her ingratitude to the memory of her former husband and the depravity she discovers in her choice of his successor, afflict his soul and cast him into utter agony'? Or with Goethe that Hamlet was another Werther? Or (as Walter Raleigh put it) that 'Hamlet is Shakespeare's study of the unpractical temperament; the portrait of a dreamer'? Or with Swinburne—who seems to have come a little nearer the mark— that 'the signal characteristic of Hamlet's inmost nature is by no means irresolution or hesitation or any form of weakness, but rather the strong conflux of contending forces'?

These and other theories, attractive as they are, go wide of the central theme of the play, which may be termed in a short phrase *a struggle for power*. It is impossible to study the character of Hamlet and remain unconvinced of the truth of Professor

Dover Wilson's comment that for his (Hamlet's) antagonist, it was essential to have a man of great cunning, since one of the main interests of the play is '*the spectacle of two extraordinarily subtle men engaged in a deadly battle of wits*'. Throughout the play the Prince and his uncle are engaged in this battle, ultimately fatal to them both.

It is the more remarkable that Shakespeare does no more than tantalize us with glimpses of 'the inmost nature' of Claudius. We see him largely through the eyes of his enemies. 'Ay, that incestuous, that adulterate beast'—so says the Ghost. And Hamlet, reeling from the Ghost's revelations, cries: 'Oh villain, villain, smiling, damnéd villain.'

We cannot but infer that, even upon so wide a canvas as *Hamlet*, Shakespeare could not find space to limn *two* such complex characters as these; the character of Claudius is left much to speculation. Even so, can anyone seriously believe that he had no redeeming qualities? Professor Dover Wilson tells us that he 'was not without courage and possessed of considerable intellectual powers' (both of which points the journal bears out) but that he 'presents nevertheless a mean and contemptible figure', which is a matter of opinion, and even within the framework of Shakespeare's play does not seem to be consistently just. Notably in one short passage the veil of prejudice is momentarily drawn aside and we catch a glimpse of the real Claudius:

> O! 'tis too true;
> How smart a lash that speech doth give my conscience!
> . . . .
> O heavy burden!

And again in the prayer scene, that most moving and least expected of all scenes in a play which is so full of surprises, we see the true character of a man, not mean and contemptible, but burdened by sin and straining towards repentance:

> Whereto serves mercy
> But to confront the visage of offence?
> And what's in prayer but this two-fold force,
> To be forestalléd, ere we come to fall,
> Or pardon'd, being down? . . . But O! what form of prayer
> Can serve my turn? . . . .
> . . . . What then? What rests?

Try what repentance can: what can it not?
Yet what can it, when one can not repent?
O wretched state! O bosom black as death!
O liméd soul that struggling to be free
Art more engaged! Help, angels! make assay;
Bow, stubborn knees; and heart with strings of steel
Be soft as sinews of the new-born babe.
All may be well.

It was at this moment that Hamlet entered and disburdened himself of a speech which Dr Johnson—that *ursa major* of the verbal bludgeon—found 'too horrible to be read or uttered'. This piece of savagery has not passed unnoticed in these annals of Elsinore.

Here in the journal Claudius testifies to the character of his much detested martial brother to whose throne he succeeded (though in circumstances markedly different from those hitherto supposed) and to the comfortable but undistinguished virtues of his erstwhile sister-in-law, the silly, amiable and sensual but courageous Gertrude. He tells us a good deal about the ageing Polonius and his forthright son Laertes and something also of Ophelia, who was evidently a pet of his. And we meet again such old friends as Rosencrantz and Guildenstern, Marcellus, Bernardo, Horatio and Osric. But, more important than any of this, the personality of Claudius himself shows starkly through the fabric of his story. So also does that of his enigmatic nephew, so long a torment to the world of scholars.

It would be otiose to cite testimonials to the authenticity of this journal from the bibliophiles of Oxford or Cambridge, Harvard, Yale or Princeton. The reader may judge for himself, as he measures the meshes of the net in which Claudius became entangled, whether or not this narrative carries more conviction than any that has yet, like the elder Hamlet's ghost, beckoned him to go away with it.

TRANSLATOR'S NOTE

The translation of this journal into the English tongue has proved a formidable task. First it was necessary to break down the code in which Claudius wrote. With modern methods this was manageable, though our labours were not eased by earlier and crude attempts to do the same. A greater impediment was Claudius's habit of changing from Danish to Latin, and occasionally to French, with little regard for syntax and sometimes more than once within the compass of a single sentence. This tiresome practice has revealed itself in a certain unevenness of style. So pronounced is this feature that it has ruggedly withstood the double process of decoding and translation: a tribute perhaps to the hand of the composer.

At some points in the narrative Claudius has made free with verbal jugglery (puns, and the like). This type of material defies literal translation and would call for tedious explanation if reproduced in the original form. Thus Hamlet made much play with the words *sun* and *son*. As appears from a footnote to the text, this was Shakespeare's version. Claudius in fact employed the Latin noun *pullus* (a chicken—doubtless used by Gertrude to her son as a term of endearment) and the adjective *pullus* (dark-coloured, blackish-grey, dusky, etc.—hence, to cite Hamlet, inky cloak). The *pullum*, incidentally, was a dark-grey garment, commonly worn by mourners and the lower orders. In this matter it has proved simpler to follow Shakespeare's lead, despite some technical inaccuracy. There is another example of this in the famous play scene, where Hamlet plays upon 'air' and 'heir'.

Setting such technical problems aside, it has been my aim to preserve so far as possible the vivacious spirit of the original manuscript. To this end I have not scrupled to employ modern usage and idiom—a proceeding for which, as I am confident, I shall be most liberally scolded.

This Narrative:

Thou liv'st; report me and my cause aright
To the unsatisfied.

Per Hamlet, Act V, Sc. 2, 331–2

. . . but 'tis not so above;
There is no shuffling, there the action lies
In his true nature. . . .

Per Claudius, Act III, Sc. 3, 60–2

Hamlet on himself:

Sir, I lack advancement.

Act III, Sc. 2, 333

Hamlet on Claudius:

Popp'd in between the election and my hopes . . .

Act V, Sc. 2, 65

Hamlet on their rivalry:

O! 'tis most sweet,
When in one line two crafts directly meet.

Act III, Sc. 4, 209–10

Claudius on Hamlet:

For like the hectic in my blood he rages . . .

Act IV, Sc. 3, 65

I

My Brother Hamlet

CHAPTER ONE

3rd March

Try as I may, I cannot stand the man. Were brothers ever
more unlike? In Denmark we have the saying that blood is
thicker than water. So it is, but the analogy is false; worse, it is
a revolting notion.

My brother Hamlet is fond of such phrases and has never
fainted at the sight of blood as I have; his natural aptitude
for the banal passes belief—perhaps it is this, above all, which
endears him to his people. There is a subtlety in this which
Polonius, that crafty old windbag, would readily perceive: the
King's subjects are indifferent to philosophy and care nothing
for statecraft, but they will applaud a platitude, provided it is
uttered with the conviction of a true believer.

Is this malicious? Most certainly. Yet at once I feel relief—
the relief of expressing myself freely in my new diary. Already
it is treasonable; so be it, and no doubt it will be more so, for
it is a measure of desperation long deferred and I turn to it
for healing and solace. Better perhaps to risk its discovery than
to change my mask of indifference and suavity at a Council of

B   3

State, or to utter in the hearing of one of Hamlet's sycophants some word of elementary truth about the present state of Denmark.

Of course, I take simple precautions. It would be more agreeable to write in clear. Even yet, after much practice, I have not fully mastered this code, the most difficult in which to compose—yet, and it is a comfort, the most difficult to break down—that I have yet used. How fortunate that I may freely write in my closet with no fear of arousing suspicion! Such has been my habit for many years and it will be readily assumed that I am again engaged upon annotating or composing another obscure and tedious work of philosophy.

It consoles me that the State system of espionage is as obsolete as the battlements of Elsinore. I am more fearful of the spoken word than the written. By the way, my nephew Hamlet, in a new and vile phrase, so typical of him, tells me he suspects that his apartments are 'bugged'. Lately he has noticed movements behind the arras, when to his certain knowledge his own servants and bodyguard were elsewhere. Not that I believe it. My nephew's mind, unlike his father's and—save the mark!— his mother Gertrude's, is so devious that it resembles nothing so much as that fabulous Danish bird, the Olé Olé, which by vulgar repute flies in ever-diminishing circles until it meets its own predestined and disreputable end. Even so it is unwise to ignore the faintest warning, whatever the source. I shall instruct Gustav tomorrow to redouble precautions against bugging of my own quarters.

15th March

Today, the eighth after the nones, is for me a black day in the calendar—Hamlet the King's birthday! He enjoys it to the full; for the rest it is a penance.

The weather, as ever, was vile and according to wont we endured the interminable parade of the soldiery, who arouse in my brother's breast God knows what ecstasies of martial ardour, in mine a surge of pity. I cannot remember a time when playing with soldiers was not his favourite pastime. On the nursery floor he played with lead soldiers by the hour; on rare occasions we would compete with opposing armies; though it bored me, it was better than having my arm twisted, and his physical strength even then was prodigious. Despite his passion for all things warlike, his tactics were—and are—rudimentary; his was an advantage of two years, an immense abyss in nursery life, but I could usually outwit him by guile: call it cheating, if you will, but there was no positive rule against a *masse de manœuvre* hidden behind the arras, any more than there is now against bugging of the palace rooms. His physical strength has stood him in good stead. I must concede it: he is every inch a king and when fully armed—that is, cap-à-pie, unbelievably his favourite mode of attire—he looks the very model of a warrior. Moreover he is blessed with an excellent circulation which seems to be proof against the rigours of the King's birthday celebrations.

We turned out as usual at eleven o'clock, and wearing as usual—nobody officially knows it, but everyone knows just the same—the light vest of chain mail which is said to be proof against assassination by any but the finest of skewers or bodkins. It has been officially tried out, and according to the best intelligence reports it will withstand the latest pattern of Norwegian missile, though understandably some of our halberdiers suffered a measure of bruising in the experiment.

Eleven o'clock may seem late enough in the day for a ceremonial parade, but I know by campaigning experience what this means to the rank and file. The order is sifted down through the ranks from the Commander-in-Chief, that master of the drill book who knows all and understands nothing, Crappswein by name, to the lowest barrack-room orderly, with precautions taken at each level of command against unpunctuality. Thus the unhappy halberdiers must rise well before dawn and have perhaps undergone four or five inspections since first light. No wonder the poor wretches, who have been on parade on and off for upwards of five hours, look gaunt and miserable, shivering in their thin uniforms as the royal entourage leaves the main gate.

A blustering north-west wind drove the sleet before it in icy gusts. Privately I have been accustomed to call this occasion *drooping* the colour, for in late years we have endured creeping damp mists over which the heavy royal standard—when it could be perceived—hung in a listless and sullen silence.

Today, for a change, it stood boldly forth from the mast; it speaks well for the training of the household cavalry that there was no breaking of the ranks as the huge wet flag spoke intermittent cannon shots from the masthead like the crack of doom.

The occasion was marred by an untoward incident, in which by ill fortune I was the central figure, though it passed over largely unobserved—even, conceivably, to the ignorant or more distant spectators to my credit. My brother, whose voice is perfectly suited to the parade ground, suffers from the delusion that in a lower register it cannot be overheard. In common with the rest of the court I was mounted, and being in my usual place—that is, to the King's left and half a stallion's length back from him—I distinctly heard him say to my sister-in-law: 'Gertrude, do try to remember you are on parade; straighten up—you look *droopy*.'

This was nearly too much for me. By an imperceptible inclination of my head I could observe Gertrude, a little to the King's right, hunched in the saddle and spreading to all points of the compass; she is no longer young and begins to prefer comfort to corsetry—also, doubtless, she was wearing her full complement of chain mail. The incongruity of the occasion and the sudden coupling of my private notion of drooping the colour with this grotesque phrase and poor Gertrude's woebegone expression caused me a moment of imbalance. To employ another new phrase of Hamlet's—my nephew of course—I felt 'choked'. That imbecile Gustav had not correctly adjusted my visor, and on a sudden movement of my head downwards it snapped shut. In reaction I touched my mount with my left spur. We have, of course, the pick of the royal stables, but this was too much even for Nimrod, who is accustomed to sleeping quietly through these ceremonials, as he has done for many years of worthy service. Before I knew where I was—or, more accurately, knowing only too well where I was—we were doing a circus act, Nimrod pawing the air and I with visor down and an excellent view of his ears, no more. Luckily two of the footguards, with some presence of mind, went to his head and brought him to earth after we had accomplished a couple of gyrations. I contrived to raise my visor again to encounter a glare from my brother—immobility on parade is a fetish with him—and a smirk from my nephew Hamlet, sitting his mount in a pose of exaggerated decorum.

After the interminable parade young Hamlet was impertinent, inscrutably as is his wont, remarking that such incidents are no more than may be expected on the ides of March and congratulating me, with affected sincerity and fervour, upon my masterly display of equestrian skill and my unruffled demeanour. This is not the first time that he has ineptly cited incidents from the life of Julius Caesar. I mentioned it to Guildenstern, knowing that he will give it a good airing round the court; if he does so and it reaches the King's ears, it is to be hoped that he will recognize the allusion.

Guildenstern, nincompoop that he is—all too like his friend Rosencrantz—puts it down to my nephew's passion for the stage. He declares that the Prince incessantly recites passages from a play about the first Caesar, in which it seems that he took the name part [1] lately at the University of Wittenberg— that hothouse of balderdash and twittery.

Imagine casting a young man of his age and figure for such a part, and such a firebrand as he, with his impetuous movements and mercurial temperament, for the part of ageing, balding Caesar, the worldly-wise master of the Roman world— soldier, statesman, cynic, gambler, pæderast! Yet I cannot but applaud the subtlety of the Wittenberg students: what greater compliment to the Prince of Denmark than to cast him for the role of imperator? And convenient too; I have not read the play [2]—but Guildenstern assures me that Brutus does away with the great Julius about the middle of it, leaving the field clear for the other players.

16th March

After the exertions of yesterday it was pleasant to repair to the palace library. There I spend much of my time, not always consulting works of reference as is commonly supposed. The library offers many advantages, of which the collection of

---

[1] As seemingly did Polonius, though there may have been some confusion of identity by William Shakespeare: see Act III, Sc. 2, 102.

[2] A simple application of chronology on the chicken and egg principle will readily satisfy the reader that this playwright cannot have been William Shakespeare.—*Ed.*

books, most of them in a deplorable condition, badly arranged, ill-indexed and mildewed, is the least. For one thing, I have never yet encountered a scion of royalty there—though I all but did so today. For another, there is Bartholomew, librarian to the household, ever indiscreet and loquacious. How he qualified for the post is a mystery; the deplorable condition of the library is a testimonial to his extramural activities.

Bartholomew assures me that the whole of the extra vote for the Quartermaster-General's office, which was to have been expended upon improvement of the quality of equipment and stores for the standing army, as lately approved by the Council of State—and of course I was the prime mover in that—has in fact been used to foster recruiting and to increase the establishment. In other words we are to have the same quality (or worse) and more quantity. Thus it is not surprising that I could detect no improvement in the uniforms or accoutrements at yesterday's parade. A nod is as good as a wink, so they say, and doubtless that is the system employed between Hamlet and that overbearing Crappswein.

The Q.M.G., a harmless individual by the name of Schmidt, will probably be sacrificed if I say anything about this. Schmidt may be safely acquitted of any complicity in it; like all other quartermasters of my acquaintance, of whatever origin, nationality or rank, his sole concern is to ensure that his books balance, whether in guns or butter. (By the way, should anyone succeed in breaking down this code, I shall not complain of being charged with an occasional and inadvertent plagiarism—not that there is so much enviable material in the palace library— but if anyone borrows from me I hope he will have breeding enough to acknowledge the source of any original phrase. If he hits on something of the kindred of 'guns and butter' by native wit that is a different matter.)

Returning to my private quarters from the library at dusk I surprised the Prince and Ophelia together in a little-frequented embrasure off the passage which I use as a short cut. I affected not to notice their presence. The Prince was self-consciously fiddling with a recorder and sitting a foot away from little Ophelia, but the affectation was not up to his usual standard. The declining day had already gilded the pair in a posture impossible to mistake before this scene had been set; it had an agreeable, almost affecting naïveté, for surely there can be nothing more innocent or appealing than the passionate raptures of the young? Ophelia, who for all her parentage and upbringing is a simple child—I like her all the better for it— was excessively *décolletée* and noticeably flushed, her neat little ears nicely matching the oriole of the sunset (women with flappy ears are an abomination). It was evident that I had surprised Hamlet in certain amorous experiments.

If this is the best that my nephew can arrange—or disarrange—with his *inamorata*, I view it on the whole with relief. At least it indicates that he is not admitted to more intimate embraces in the palace or the household of Polonius; in either place the political implications could be formidable! All the same I do not find it acceptable that he should pursue the affair in such a squalid manner. Bartholomew tells me that the young people of a certain set—he is too tactful to define it— now term this pastime 'snogging'; I am indebted to him for much invaluable intelligence.

18th March

I am honoured by an invitation to dine with Polonius tomorrow. Such occasions are rare, and with good reason. Nobody knows for certain how the King's younger brother fits into the State of Denmark—least of all he, wry thought!—yet everyone may be sure that an invitation, visit or colloquy will be the subject of espionage, report, speculation and ill-informed comment. Young and spirited bachelors of good family never satisfy the insatiable demand; even the dullest of the species will serve to equalize the sexes or at worst will provide stimulus for our jowly Danish matrons. But the middle-aged bachelor is *persona non grata*—usually a misfit, a bore or a crank. Add the taint of royalty to one who is suspected of being all three and you have by definition such a guest as only the King's chief minister could venture to invite.

19th March

I will concede that Polonius keeps a good table and does not stint his guests; moreover his taste in Rhenish is impeccable. Had it been an official dinner I should have deemed it more politic to decline unless my brother had been invited and had accepted. As it was I was assured that it was not even D.O.— that is, demi-official; just a private dinner for a couple of dozen guests at most.

With consummate tact Polonius had included Penelope amongst the guests. (I had, of course, assured myself beforehand that she would be there. I have my own small system of intelligence and do not care to be taken by surprise, even in minor society affairs.) The arrangements were admirable: Penelope was accompanied by a nonentity whom I recognized after a while as Flipp, a second secretary in the Foreign Office, doubtless impressed by Polonius for the occasion. He had evidently been well briefed—or perhaps it comes naturally to his vocation—for he was always at Penelope's side when required but contrived to make himself scarce whenever there was a chance of my speaking to her privately. He is plainly deserving of promotion, and I must see what can be done about it.

By good fortune, or the discretion of Flipp, I had a minute or two with Penelope before the main body of guests arrived (in Denmark it is considered bad form for the chief guest to arrive last). She contrived to communicate to me that both Laertes and the old doctor, her great-uncle Stavridos, would be seeking unofficial audiences in the course of the evening. Dr Stavridos has been physician to the royal household for as long as I can remember. It is with an effort that I remind myself that Penelope is his great-niece on the distaff side; she is of course a Papparigopoulos. Why this Greek family deserted their native and milder clime and softer manners to endure the mists and rheumatics of Elsinore is an enigma; I must remember to ask the old doctor about it.

I begin to realize that I depend upon Penelope for more than—shall we say—the modest creature comforts of a bachelor. Like Bartholomew she is a mine of information. Not that she belongs to my small circle of intelligence staff (I had all but written 'espionage', but there is a world of difference!): she would be consumed with mirth at the notion. If Penelope has a fault—none, certainly, of face or figure—it is an irrepressible urge to poke fun at the lumpish conventions of the Danish court; this is not only irresponsible but dangerous. I forget—

another failing has sprung to mind: a tendency to jump to conclusions with no intermediate process of ratiocination. On this I have rallied her more than once. With that species of feminine logic which so absurdly equates *post hoc* with *propter hoc*, she replies that she is usually right. That this is unanswerable does not make it any less vexatious.

It turned out as Penelope had warned me, except that instead of there being two separate audiences I found myself between the old doctor and Laertes, who made, as it were, a pincer movement (I find it hard to avoid using my brother's outworn military jargon in political contexts—for one thing they go down so well at the Council of State).

The old doctor is shrewd and laconic, his eyes still penetrative under a jungly thatch of jutting eyebrows, matching the curlicues from his hirsute ears. Laertes, as ever, is forthright and blunt in his manner, though how he has contrived to be so, with such a devious father, passes my comprehension.

In all this I detect the mind and hand of Polonius directing the manœuvre with his accustomed craft and attention to detail. Stavridos is above suspicion; Laertes, his own son, as he pays respects to the principal guest, should surely arouse none? Yet the stakes must be high or the impasse great, for would Polonius entrust such a mission, even in part, to his own son were it otherwise? None knows better than he, in his high place, that he and his household have far to fall.

A private dinner-party would not seem ideal for discussion of secret matters of State. It is doubtless for this reason that Polonius picked upon this choice method. Enough for me to be seen strolling with Laertes in the palace rose garden and speculation would be rife: the more so as we shall see no roses until June. Just to ensure that our conference could not be overheard, our host thoughtfully placed the doctor next to the musicians. Before I could size up the situation I found myself sitting next to him with Laertes on the other side. The doctor becomes hard of hearing and Laertes has no ear; would that I enjoyed either or both of these natural advantages!

My head swims tonight with flageolets and trumpets, and perhaps a little with Rhenish and the effort of penetrating the designs of my brother's chief minister. It is already late and to encode more would be heavy labour. I shall sleep well, I hope. If sleepless, I may rest; if restless, I shall think. There is much to be thought upon.

20th March

In vino veritas may serve as a saw for commoners. Princes of the blood royal are educated in a sterner school which enjoins ever-increasing caution with each potation. It amuses me to observe how I skirted round the problem in my jottings yesterday. Now in full sobriety let me state it boldly: it is none other than my nephew Hamlet's health—I use a colourless word—and by implication the health of Denmark.

For long I have suspected that something is seriously amiss with my nephew. These extremes of emotion, outbursts of violence alternating with philosophic calm; furious resentment of supposed slights and insults, with trifles magnified and distorted, arrogance succeeded by humility; a swift apprehension and vivid imagination, yet a failure to perceive true proportion: all this and with it a boyish charm—is it any wonder that he is for ever in the public eye?

Why should I be so much disturbed by the knowledge that my own apprehensions are shared? Is it worse to have fears confirmed than to have them aroused? Yes—the tumour may be of a night's imagining until the physician (Stavridos again!) gives it substance and form. Then it becomes malignant, an evil portent—a portent, I ask, for what?

Laertes asserts that my nephew's extravagances at Wittenberg have passed far beyond the bounds traditionally conceded to high-spirited students, and yet again beyond those—at a further remove—set for princes of the blood royal. There were instances so characteristic as to be unmistakable: I shall not waste time encoding them. According to Laertes, garbled versions, which lose nothing in narration, already circulate in the palace precincts.

I made the obvious point: what has all this to do with me? (The doctor raised a stag-beetle eyebrow in a half-circle to the German horn.[1]) Why does not Laertes—or, better still, his

---

[1] Not to be confused with the French horn, of much later date. Claudius probably refers to the *crumhorn*, introduced *circa* 1500. The tone is said to have a strongly humming nasal quality and would doubtless have been ideal for the purpose of frustrating eavesdroppers.—*Ed.*

father—put these questions to the King? If not to the King, then to the Queen?

One asks these questions; it is part of the routine. The old doctor answered in his terse manner: 'It is impossible to believe that Your Highness does not know the answers to these questions.'

It is true that I know the answers. My brother declines to discuss any question remotely concerned with the succession; he has an invincible belief in his own immortality. The Queen submits in everything to him and dotes on the Prince. Such a combination would undo any tale-bearer, save perhaps one so close to the throne as myself.

I cautiously asked the doctor's opinion. He says these extremes of emotion are familiar to the medical profession and may commonly be traced to the lesions of infancy or childhood. The Prince has been subjected to unusual stresses and strains: his father has been too severe, his mother too indulgent; he has undergone without stint the Spartan discipline which is the lot of royal princes (did I not suffer likewise?), yet alternatively and by spasms he has been accorded the licence of a libertine.

I hinted that too much should not be made of youthful aberrations; it seems likely that the Prince will settle down. It should be no great matter for astonishment, I said, that the unaccustomed liberty of Wittenberg should have encouraged him to certain unseemly excesses. And I suggested that it might prove for the best that he should extrude these poisons from his system before he is of an age and responsibility to infect the State of Denmark.

These observations were, need I say, as 'springes to catch woodcocks' and Laertes responded in his faithful manner. It is unfortunate, so he says, that Hamlet has formed certain undesirable attachments at Wittenberg, notably one with young Fortinbras of Norway. Opinion is divided upon its origin and significance. Some say the friendship is political, others that it is natural, and a few (there are always a few of those) who uncharitably suggest it is unnatural. In my opinion these several views throw more light on the persons expressing them than on the mercurial Prince or his motives and actions.

It seems that the Prince's supporters think it progressive— even amusing—that he should be on friendly terms with the heir-presumptive to old Norway. Laertes and his party on the other hand hold it nothing short of treason to fraternize with our hereditary enemy; they call the Prince's faction the Primrose League. (What the Prince's set call the frumpish party of Laertes I have yet to learn; doubtless Bartholomew or Penelope will enlighten me.)

I reserve my opinion on the Prince's activities, but the fanciful name Primrose League argues a homely wit, in some unknown supporter of the adverse party, of which the stalwart Laertes is certainly innocent. It is easy to recognize an allusion to an outworn refrain of Polonius with which all will be familiar who have suffered the elder statesman's tedious discourses:

> Whiles like a puff'd and reckless libertine,
> Himself the *primrose path* of dalliance treads
> And recks not his own rede.

This must indeed be a common figure of speech, for I have even heard dear, pretty, ingenuous little Ophelia quote it with a smile.

Note: Stavridos says one thing is certain: Hamlet's health will either improve or deteriorate. As to a cure he is enigmatic: 'When the kettle boils, best take it off the fire.'

He advises me to read again the fable of Oedipus. In common with most of the Greek mythology I find it repulsive and shall not follow his advice.

CHAPTER TWO

23rd March

For the last three days Denmark has been seized in the icy grip of winter. It might well be late January: three feet of snow and sledges on the road—where it may still be discerned—and young skaters on the waterways. All this would be more acceptable with a sparkle of sunshine; instead we endure a howling north-east wind which piles the snow in treacherous drifts against a leaden sky.

This unseasonable weather has moved me to have words again with the Ministry of Works about the central heating system which I ordered for my apartments last autumn. This new device is regarded by some as a fad and by others (my brother Hamlet included) as a craven indulgence. For myself I view it as an insurance against the unspeakable Danish climate, at worst as a painless method of committing suicide.

The work required of the Ministry is minimal: no more than to construct a modest furnace in the basement and a few vents at floor level in the principal rooms and sundry grills (not too many) for ventilation, with connecting ducts. Bartholomew tells me that the chief engineer has cold feet—if the term is allowable—by reason of the number of householders who have succumbed to the fumes of the standard installation. This evidently alarms the ministry; for myself, given the choice, I prefer to expire of asphyxiation rather than of frostbite.

25th March

What one might expect: a sudden thaw and reports on all hands of feckless people drowned—sad sacrifices to the caprice of our climate and their own improvidence.

I am forcibly reminded of that disagreeable campaign which redounds so much to my martial brother's credit, when—by popular repute—he smote the sledded Polack on the ice. This exploit has long since passed into official history and, worse, into balladry. It is otiose for me, a mere eye-witness, to contend against such powerful forces. But I owe it to the unknown decoder of this journal—strange that already I assume his existence!—to contradict these absurdities.

Be it known, then, that the celebrated sledded Polacks were no more than a parcel of mercenaries [1] engaged to support the army of the late King Fortinbras of Norway. If the truth be told, they were in some difficulty in trying to manœuvre Norwegian sledges of a new and unfamiliar design. The Polacks were the worst equipped of the forces arrayed against us in what has come to be known as 'the winter war'. For the same reason it was against them that we mounted such attacks as we were capable of. The campaign, of which I have all too vivid and painful a memory, opened ill for the Danish forces,

---

[1] At this time Denmark included most of southern Sweden as we now know it. Claudius refers twice in this context to the Poles as mercenaries, evidently to show his contempt for them. (We discount the theory that the Polacks were Muscovites.)

It seems more probable that the Poles were *allies* of the Norwegians. Copenhagen, which was protected at the entrance to the sound by the battlements of Elsinore, had been chosen as the capital in the year 1443. At this time it would have been at about the centre of King Hamlet's dominions. The distance from Copenhagen to Oslo (then Christiania) as the crow flies—if it does, up the Kattegat—is by fifty miles or so *longer* than the distance so measured from Copenhagen to Danzig.

Such an alliance between Norway and Poland against Denmark has its counterpart in the traditional combination of Scotland and France against England before the Act of Union.—*Ed.*

as our campaigns invariably do. We were badly provisioned, slow to react, ill served by our intelligence and (one might as well admit it) thoroughly out-generalled.

According to all decent convention the season for campaigning is the summer; even the great Julius, whom my nephew is so fond of aping, accepted the hibernian truce and recognized the convenience of winter quarters. But the Norwegians, having occupied themselves through the previous summer and autumn constructing and stock-piling engines of war—sledges, snow-shoes, pick-axes, crampons and other devices (to say nothing of an immense consignment of woollen combination underwear, specially imported from the English mills), treacherously launched their assault in mid February, thinking to overwhelm us in a short campaign of four to six weeks. Happily, though Thor is a stern master, he distributes logistic disorder with an even hand: muddles were generously multiplied in the enemy lines of communication by the novelty of a winter campaign and weak liaison with their Polack mercenaries. Had it not been so, we should infallibly have been overwhelmed.

It was in fact the mightier Thaw who finally settled the issue. Suddenly, unheralded and unusually early, winter turned to spring. It was Thaw himself, in all his majesty, who smote the sledded Polack on the ice, turning all to confusion, bogging down the transport and drowning many. My brother made a virtue of necessity and at his command we escorted the retreating army at a distance consistent with a semblance of pursuit—that is to say, at a safe distance—for fully ten miles.

Such was the winter war which has given rise to this egregious legend.

26th March

I am summoned to a Council of State, convened for the day after tomorrow. Not that I am a member of the Council— an adviser at most. I never attend but when invited, and being seldom invited, seldom attend; when invited, needless to say I attend. This is what I term Polonius language, or *Polonaise.* I make a point of practising it before Council meetings, the better to understand the elder statesman's convoluted periods.

The court buzzes with rumour of riots in Norway. My brother will doubtless affect to perceive a threat to the stability of Denmark! It remains to be seen whether these disorders differ, either in principle or degree, from those which have tormented the Norwegian people ever since the death of King Fortinbras. True, he held them in an iron grip and they suffered greatly from his emulate pride and ambition. Yet now they groan and suffer the more for other causes. Old Norway, brother to Fortinbras, is ailing and weak; worse, young Fortinbras is by all accounts of unimproved mettle hot and full—a veritable nephew Hamlet, yet without my nephew's amiable qualities and with none of his complexities.

Once again my thoughts turn to the winter war. Perhaps my casual jottings of yesterday were prescient? The Danish ballad has it that my brother slew the elder Fortinbras in mortal combat, which is vulgarly understood to mean single combat, though in this day and age nothing could be more absurd. A likeable young man—so he was then, but I have to remind myself that he is now Poet Laureate and greying at the temples—was bidden to eulogize the winter war; in his distress he sought my advice. I assured him that pedantic adherence to fact and literal interpretation of events are not demanded of poets, still less of ballad-writers. Fortified by my counsel he was emboldened to ignore a few inconvenient features—for example, that Fortinbras, as it happens, contracted a severe chill towards the end of his ill-advised campaign and expired of pneumonia in Christiania some weeks after his troops had been disbanded.

So be it; we should weigh the consequences of our actions and I have nobody but myself to blame for the substance (though I disown the style) of the resulting concoction with which we are all so sickeningly familiar:

> Dar'd to the combat; in which our valiant Hamlet—
>   For so this side of our known world esteem'd him—
> Did slay this Fortinbras . . . .

But so he did in a way, of course. And a big mistake it has proved. By all accounts conditions in Norway are chaotic.

27th March

Laertes, returning once more to Paris, came to take his leave—
a courtesy unlikely to arouse more than mild interest among
the palace spies. The occasion being semi-official, I thought
fit to give orders that my public audience room be put in
readiness. As a happy afterthought, some few minutes before
Laertes was due I alerted my new warning system, thinking
to take Gustav by surprise. In this aspiration I certainly failed,
for the alarm bells rang instantly and insistently all over my
wing of the palace and continued without intermission for what
seemed an eternity.

After a while Gustav arrived in a comical state of concern
mixed with sweating frenzy, still buckling on his sword and all
but tripping over it. He was accompanied by three or four
members of my kitchen staff, wearing expressions of bovine
intrepidity. I sternly ordered an immediate and thorough
search of the apartments.

Unbelievably an alleged miscreant was run to earth in the
Brown Gallery, or to be more precise fell backwards out of a
press which one of my young scullions opened out of idle
curiosity. This created great jubilation amongst my home
guard (as I call them) and the unlucky man was brought
before me in a condition of abject terror.

It seems, according to his story, that he was sent by the
Ministry of Works to measure the Brown Gallery for the
central heating system, but was put in fear by the sudden
peal of bells and leapt incontinently into the nearest closet.
I listened to his faltering narrative with every appearance of
disbelief and a mounting impatience which I had no cause to
counterfeit (I suspected, as it turns out with reason, that the
dinner was burning). So I dismissed him to my private dungeon
to cool his heels whilst his credentials are checked; I must
remember to let him out this evening.

Mainly this farce is to encourage Gustav and his unmilitary
posse to renewed vigilance, but as it has turned out it will also
serve to remind the Ministry that the Brown Gallery was
specifically *excluded* from my specification for the central heating
—a point I shall not fail to drive home.

Laertes arrived soon after these alarums and excursions; it

c

was with difficulty that I extracted from him an important
covert message from Polonius. The burden of the message is
that Polonius has been overruled by the King in the matter
of Norwegian policy for discussion at the Council tomorrow
and he trusts I shall not hold him responsible for it.

Am I to believe this or not? The old fox covers many trails;
in his old age he begins, perhaps, to resemble a squirrel more
nearly than a fox, for sometimes, as I truly believe, he forgets
where he has buried his nuts.

28th March

Council of State, a memorable day. Tomorrow I shall dictate
my own minutes to my confidential secretary; the court minutes
are not to be trusted. Tonight I am overwhelmed with fatigue.

29th March

Van Loon has taken down a full note of the Council meeting
and is to transcribe it himself. He is a fast and accurate
amanuensis and never presumes to sub-edit; it is an additional
consolation that he has but a dim notion of the purport of
what he transcribes. All the same I see to it that his shorthand
notes (as he calls them) are destroyed in my presence and that
he transcribes but one copy—my own—of any secret paper.

My dictated minutes are factual; I reserve comment for my
journal. War! That, in one short ominous word, is my brother
Hamlet's policy. As I expected, he professes apprehension lest
the disorders in Norway should overrun the frontier and infect
the state of Denmark. Such disingenuous reasoning consorts ill
with his bluff manner and earthy character; doubtless a syco-
phant has suggested the argument.

That notable strategist Crappswein supported the monarch
with alternative but inconsequential arguments. He asked us
to take note of the present plight of a divided and distraught
nation and recommended that we grasp the golden moment to
overwhelm it in a short—and one must presume, near blood-
less—summer campaign. Already he sees himself a great power
in the land—in two lands—with the yet unminted Norwegian
star (first class) glittering upon his breast.

My brother's ambitions are equally puerile but more nebulous. He tires of the routine of the court and of the imponderables and subtleties of government. He sees himself cap-à-pie again, with beaver down.

Predictably Polonius treated us to a *tour de force*. He circled round the problem with all the expertise of that fabulous fowl, the Olé Olé, and his discourse would scarcely have been endurable had it not been well seasoned with *Polonaise*. To my amusement I could see that he was flattered by my earnest attention; in fact I was noting down for private entertainment the richer nuggets of his fancy. According to him—though in this instance I suspect that he has borrowed the phrase from that young spark Horatio, bosom friend and fellow student of my nephew Hamlet—young Fortinbras has 'shark'd up a list of lawless resolutes for food and diet to some enterprise that hath a stomach in 't'. In other words he has indiscriminately swept up a band of sanguinary outlaws seeking a spice of adventure.

This is heady stuff indeed—if the metaphor will pass—but the drift of it escapes me. Are we seriously to suppose that this young reprobate Fortinbras is a menace to Denmark? Or merely a factious nuisance and a thorn in the side of old Norway, impotent and bed-rid? One thing is clear: from the oratory of Polonius we may draw—and are doubtless intended to draw—such conclusions as best consort with our own prejudices.

30th March

Still troubled by the portentous but inconclusive debate of the Council of State, I decided to relax with Penelope for the evening—a remedy for ill humour which had never yet failed me. But the time is out of joint and today was one of those when one strives with a personal (I suspect a Lutheran) devil.

Nothing at first disturbed our accustomed ease, though indeed Penelope's movements seemed a trifle brisker, her eyes perceptibly brighter, her responses a fraction more rapid than usual. Her manservant came and went with his wonted dexterity, silent and unobtrusive. The dinner was exquisite, the wine a perfect choice.

Later Penelope lay languid on her couch in the firelight; Elsinore was banished—at least it had receded. Perhaps a little relaxed also—are we not slaves to our creature comforts?—I was imprudent enough to lean over her with some amorous pleasantry. Thus did I shatter the calm of the evening.

'Claudius, not tonight. We have serious matters to talk about.'

I groaned. 'Have I not suffered abundantly from the Council? Let us forget serious matters for a while.'

She sat bolt upright and released my arm from her shoulder.

'Claudius, I have seen the minutes; I pray you not to ask me how it comes about that I have seen them.'

Flipp? I wondered. No; he would not have had access to them; had he seen them he would not have dared to divulge them. A host of conjectures raced through my brain, but I abandoned them to further reflection.

'Very well,' I said; 'I shall not ask. What of it?'

'Claudius dear, how could you be such a *fool*?'

I sat myself down again by the fire and the room was silent except for the spluttering of the logs. I waited for her to continue. There was a long silence. At last she said impatiently:

'The King is a stupid fool; you, Claudius, are a clever fool. Of the two the clever fool is worse. His follies are the greater and his friends the fewer.'

'This is treasonable talk,' I said.

She made a characteristic gesture, not signally polite. My vexation subsided in laughter.

'Very well,' I said; 'the clever fool is the worse. You may well be right. But why all this sound and fury?'

I do not know what answer I expected; Penelope is unpredictable.

'Listen,' she said, and proceeded to recite the official minutes, word-perfect, as follows:

' "His Royal Highness the Prince Claudius, adviser to the Council, said he had listened with growing consternation to the thesis of the General Crappswein, Commander-in-Chief of the Danish Forces, and with bewilderment to the address of the Chief Minister.

' "What was the purpose of this expedition to Norway? Is Norway a land flowing with milk and honey? Is it a desirable

prize to be won? Has it sheep, cattle, crops in abundance? No;
it is a country of fjords, ice and snow, inhospitable, remote,
useless to Denmark; moreover the climate is vile.

' "His Highness ventured to remind the Commander-in-Chief
that an eminent general, by name Moses, had not dispensed
with reconnaissance despite assurances given by Jah himself.
Joshua, the son of Nun, and Caleb, the son of Jephunneh, had
been dispatched to spy out the land and had returned in safety
with a favourable report. His Highness would advise the General
to single out and train a Joshua and a Caleb for a like mission
in Norway, though he feared he could give no guarantee of an
equally favourable result.

' "There had been talk of infection; the best way of avoiding
infection was to keep clear of it. [*Laughter.*] The Norwegian
people resembled their country: rugged, riven, divided, stubborn and intractable.

' "His Highness paid tribute to the King Hamlet's acknow-
ledged and meritorious prowess in the field. It was not for
nothing that His Majesty was known to his loyal people in the
indelible words of a stirring ballad—now part of our national
heritage—as 'our valiant Hamlet' . . . ."

'Claudius, you could not have said that!'
'The minutes, for once, are correct,' I said, gloomily.
Penelope smoothed down her dress with an impatient move-
ment as though to remove a crease, and continued:

' "But His Royal Highness feared that if the predictions of
the Commander-in-Chief were to be credited, the campaign
would prove a sad disillusionment. Both the King and the
General were fire-eaters. They were going to a land of snow and
ice where no fire was. They were seeking glory in battle against
a worthy foe. But the Fates had been unkind. There was no
worthy foe: no more was to be found there than a sick old man
and his renegade nephew who had shark'd up a list of lawless
resolutes. . . ."

'Where, may I ask, did you borrow *that* vile phrase?'
'From Polonius,' said I. 'You would not know the allusion;
it was really quite apposite.'
'I have no doubt.'
'Need we go on with this recital?' I said. 'You seem to have
learnt it pretty well by heart, and to tell you the truth I thought
the official minutes were closer to the mark than they usually are.'

She looked sad.

'Oh, Claudius dear, will you never understand? Can you not perceive the danger in which you stand, which you bring closer to yourself all the time by this foolery? You still think this speech was good?'

'A bit overdone perhaps,' I said. 'You must not be too censorious. I did not even know what was to be discussed.'

'It is as well,' she said; 'you would have made it a thousand times worse.'

To my amazement she burst into tears.

CHAPTER THREE

6th April

Greatly troubled by a letter delivered into my hand by one whom I recognize to be a secret agent of Polonius—by name Voltimand. He is well known and esteemed at court, so it is to be hoped that his indiscretion in passing me the letter with none of the usual precautions will not arouse suspicion. The message purports to come from old Norway himself, written in his own hand. Either it is an excellent forgery or (as I think more probable) it is genuine; certainly both the handwriting and the turns of phrase are familiar to me.

Though little more than a week has elapsed since the Council meeting, Norway professes to have seen a synopsis of the minutes. I can well believe it; the Norwegian espionage is excellent, which is only to say that our counter-espionage is deplorable. After all, if Penelope, in a private station, is able to quote the minutes verbatim two days after the session, is it any cause for wonder that the old King in Christiania has them soon afterwards?

The burden of Norway's message is the folly of perpetuating

the traditional strife between our peoples—a proposition to which I most cordially assent. He complains bitterly of the contumacious Fortinbras and accuses my nephew Hamlet, in the most immoderate terms, of what he is pleased to describe as complicity in 'the revolt'. Is our news censored or is the situation in Norway more unsettled than I had supposed? Or is the old man, in his enfeebled condition, making a mountain out of a molehill?

As for the charge against Hamlet, whose subtlety far exceeds that of Norway and Fortinbras put together, at first I was disposed to dismiss it out of hand or to put it down to the disordered perspective and understandable malice of a troubled old man. But I begin to wonder. Disparate as their temperaments are, the two young men have at least one thing in common, that is, a clear understanding of the principle of *cui bono*. Each, being heir-presumptive to a throne, would wish, one may be sure, to erase the ugly word 'presumptive'; for, need one say, the presumption is of electoral accord to the succession, and no more in Norway than in Denmark does the crown devolve as of right by lineal succession. If it did, young Fortinbras would now sit upon the throne of Norway. 'Help me to my throne and in due time I will help you to yours.' Could these be the words of Fortinbras, put into his mouth by Hamlet at Wittenburg, of which we are now witnessing the first-fruits? There is much to ponder here.

Be this as it may, Norway flatters me by supposing that I have any control of the destiny of Denmark. Agreement upon general principles is one thing: ability to apply them quite another. The imbecilities of Crappswein carry more conviction with my brother than any considerations of logic or logistics. Worse still, as Penelope evidently thinks, I may even have furthered this lunacy by an ill-considered opposition to it.

As for Polonius, it is evident that, as his hold on life diminishes, he grips more firmly to office; thus does a man clutching at the barnacled rocks lacerate his palms ere he falls headlong in the sea. His dilemma is fearful, for in truth he knows full well, by long experience and that extra sense which is innate in such a statesman as he, that this is an idiot policy for Denmark; yet to oppose the King in his present humour is to court annihilation. Forgetful and wandering as he sometimes now shows himself, his tenacity and resource are beyond compare. Let another do the dirty work for him, and who better than the Prince Claudius? Well, we shall see.

7th April

Cornelius, whom I recognize as another in the pay of Polonius, visited me upon some pretext concerning the order of precedence at palace functions, which serves to remind me that I am bidden to attend the King's accession celebrations a week hence. Over a long period I have cultivated a system of repression so that I do not have to contemplate the odious for one moment longer than is inevitable; but the unfortunate Cornelius was not to know that he had disorganized my regimen.

Palace protocol is not the concern of the Lord Chamberlain (an archaic title by which Polonius likes to be known and of which he is inordinately vain) but for the Master of the Household. I could not but feel a little affronted that he should send Cornelius to me upon such a thin pretext—surely he overestimates my obtuseness?

After a while Cornelius inquired obliquely whether I had any message to communicate in reply to one that I had lately received from Voltimand. He was painfully disoriented when I told him that the message I had received from Voltimand was either a forgery and not fit to be answered, or authentic, in which case it would be treason to reply to it. Presently he departed, bewildered and shaken. I could wish I were there, but invisible, when he makes his report to Polonius.

None of this helps to solve the problem of Norway's message. What to do? Reply? If so, in what terms? Ignore it? Report it to the King? Confront Polonius with it? I cannot see my way clearly; therefore I shall do nothing. There is no decision of greater spiritual comfort than this—to do nothing.

8th April

Vexatious bill from the Ministry of Works for 'overtime' which I was lucky enough to notice and connect with the incident in the Brown Gallery some ten days ago; otherwise it would doubtless have been debited to my household account. This is their method of intimating, in a roundabout way, that they do not care to have a member of their staff incarcerated on suspicion of spying.

I told van Loon to return the account with a note saying that the unfortunate man is not blameworthy because nature has not endowed him with the same nerve as his employers. He is to add—in the third-party mode of correspondence which adds tone, but no sense, to palace minutes—that this is the only warmth yet kindled in His Royal Highness's quarters by the central heating department of the Ministry.

9th April

That miserable downcast old man torments my conscience. 'There is no decision of greater spiritual comfort than this—to do nothing.' Those are the words I set down not forty-eight hours ago, yet now I look at them and they mock me. Replace 'nothing' by 'something'—ah, then you have it! To do something, no matter what, be it right or wrong, prudent or injudicious, then you have relief from the intolerable burden of inaction and indecision.

With many misgivings and no small labour I penned a reply. In such an enterprise I dared not trust even to the faithful van Loon. I drafted and redrafted it several times—a sure sign that one does not know one's own mind, and all the more vexing because as a general rule I say what I have to say and have done with it. However, at length I reduced it to sufficiently non-committal terms (as I thought); then I had to copy and recopy it and dispose of the original drafts. I cursed Polonius for saddling me with a task so much better suited to his own capabilities.

Finally, not without contrivance, I handed the message covertly to Voltimand, with orders that it be delivered by express and in all secrecy into the hand of the old King. Voltimand is to be trailed by a competent and tried member of my own information service. I hinted as much. Should I have done so? It is hard to say.

12th April

I gave it out that I was indisposed, kept to my bed and sent for Stavridos. He examined me thoroughly and pronounced me perfectly fit. I said I was relieved to hear it, but prevention was better than cure, and I might well be ill the day after tomorrow. It is not for nothing that Stavridos is the court physician; it was with no more than a momentary hesitation that he took the point: that in two days' time I must attend upon the sovereign in full regalia; a genuine ailment then would take on the semblance of malingering; thus it is wiser to counterfeit indisposition now, lest the true be taken for counterfeit later.

I hinted to the doctor that my condition might admit of a glass of wine if in conscience he could prescribe it, and perhaps he would care to join me. He nodded assent in his curt fashion. I pulled the bell-rope and sank back on the pillows as Gustav appeared. The doctor said:

'His Royal Highness must be fortified by wine. Pray send up a bottle of dry sack from the cellar and see that it is not over-chilled.'

'Two glasses,' I murmured faintly from my bed of sickness; 'one for the doctor.'

Gustav contrived to combine a glance of sympathy for the patient with one of deference to the doctor and retired on the balls of his feet, creating more creak but less clatter than is his wont. Stavridos turned towards the window, doubtless to conceal his amusement; though abrupt, he is the soul of courtesy.

After a while, when the wine had been brought, I touched on the subject of my nephew Hamlet's health. The doctor was reluctant to express an opinion, saying it was not permissible to discuss the health of one patient with another.

'Except publicly and against a background of flageolets and trumpets,' I said mischievously and by way of reminder.

'It is not a distinction of place but of topic,' said the doctor. 'The Prince Hamlet's health—that is one thing; his disposition —shall we say—is another.'

'His humours,' I said.

'I will concede that his humours do not come within the purview of the Hippocratic oath,' he admitted.

'But the body and mind are two halves of one whole—would you not agree, doctor?' said I, just to test him as *advocatus diaboli*.

The doctor began to cheer up. There is nothing he likes better than to pursue the indefinable over hill and dale.

'A layman's view, Your Highness, if I may say so; shall we say that they are two aspects of the same whole—artificially distinguished by our crude dichotomy?'

I could see we were getting along famously. He ruminated for a while and then added:

'Be it understood that I minister to the bodily needs of my patients. There are doctors in Alexandria and elsewhere, I am told, who have studied what is called the *psyche*. I have no professional knowledge of such matters; I may therefore speak of them, I conceive, with freedom.'

'The less we know, the more we speak,' I said.

He took a turn round the room and returned to his wine, saying: 'I shall break my rule and divulge a professional secret: the Prince Hamlet's health is excellent.'

'That is good,' I said. 'Yet I hear he has bad dreams.'

'Did you read Oedipus again?' he asked.

'Certainly not; mythology is far from my taste, doctor.' Goading him on, I added: 'Primitive garbage.'

He twisted the glass in his hand, studying the rich colour of the wine against the light. I could see that my bait of falsehood would take his carp of truth. To encourage him I promised I would again read the trilogy of Sophocles, though it was open to doubt that I should be thereby edified. And, just to disabuse him of any notion that I had forgotten the detestable fable, I added that I was no Oedipus—meaning (need I say it?) that I could not compete with him who divined the riddle of the Sphinx and thereby delivered Thebes. The doctor was gratified by my allusion; though whether it was his recognizing the truth of my admission or the form in which I had chosen to express it which pleased him the more, I cannot say.

'It is evident', I said, pursuing a temporary advantage, 'that you discern some resemblance between the condition of Thebes and the state of Denmark, though I confess it escapes me. Moreover if you are comparing Oedipus himself with my nephew Hamlet, I must own that I perceive no justice in it.'

This last statement was not strictly true—merely a hone on which the doctor might sharpen his wit, but he remained silent, so I continued:

'Surely the child was named Oedipus on account of his swollen *feet*.'

A flicker passed over the old man's countenance. I watched him narrowly as he compared in his mind's eye the possibilities of tumescence at either extremity of the human frame. But the diplomat was now paramount. Diving away from the political implications, he remarked, with seeming inconsequence:

'Your Highness well knows that the ancients recognized four elements—fire, air, water and earth.'

'Aristotle, following Empedocles of Sicily,' said I, not to be outdone. 'Not to mention a fifth, the *quinta essentia* or quintessence.'

'True, but I do not speak now of the material significance of the elements; my overlong service to Aesculapius has taught me many things, not least that the human spirit is compounded of like elements, of which one or another is commonly dominant in each of us.'

'I trust we are still on a non-professional plane,' said I, suppressing my laughter lest Gustav should appear with restoratives and strike a discordant note.

'Indeed yes, Your Highness; this is no more than a foible of mine; a little wandering of a mind wearied of the natural course of nature and the vulgarity of nostrums and potions.'

'Well, let us apply your theory,' I said. 'Of what elements would you say that I am compounded?'

'Delve in your memory and Your Highness will dredge up the answer,' said he; 'tell me how the Danish lawyers define a reservoir, a lake or an estuary?'

'Earth covered with water,' I replied instantly, not a little pleased to air my knowledge of the law.

'Ah, I knew that Your Highness would not fail me.'

'Now it is your turn,' I said. 'The King?'

'Earth,' he replied.

'Very good, but lacking in precision; granite, not fibrous loam. Now what about the Queen?'

'It is your turn, Your Highness,' he reminded me.

'Air,' I said; 'but this is too easy. And now it is your turn. I will give you the Prince.'

He looked sombre and there was a long silence. He shifted uneasily in his chair by the bed and pulled the lobe of his ear so that the curlicues danced a little free waltz and then, after a brief tremble, stood still again, like the figures on a musical box.[1]

'Fire,' he said at length. 'And what is the inmost nature of fire?'

To this also I knew the answer.

'It consumes or is by itself consumed,' I said, answering parrot-wise, like a well-schooled child.

He smiled with a winning sadness of comprehension.

I pulled the bell-rope.

'The patient is tired,' he said to Gustav, as he took his leave.

13th April

Stavridos called again and pronounced me convalescent. It seems that with cosseting I may be in shape for the palace wassail tomorrow. To dispel my melancholy he said he would prescribe for me again in the evening, but I must rest; official visitors are banned. As a token of my submission to his ruling I offered my engagement calendar for his inspection and he entered 'Doctor's Prescription' in his crabwise hand against the hour of six o'clock.

Shortly after six his great-niece Penelope arrived and Gustav had the good sense to admit her; more probably, on second thoughts, he was acting, as I am, under doctor's orders.

'I hope it is nothing infectious,' she said, whirling in with a great draught, kissing me on the forehead and dumping a large bunch of grapes on the nearest chair.

'Have you brought the prescription?' I asked.

'In my person,' she said.

---

[1] This metaphor has aroused scepticism among certain scholars, but plainly Claudius was acquainted with a musical box topped by dancing figures, doubtless of cruder design than those which became fashionable in the eighteenth century. It is not without interest that Henry VIII included in his musical equipment '*a Virginal that goethe with a whele without playing uponn*'. And in 1599 Queen Elizabeth sent to the Sultan of Turkey, amongst other gifts, an organ with carillon combined, built by Thomas Dallam, whose description of the device includes the following:

'*Then the musicke went of, and the orgon played a song of five partes twyse over. In the tope of the orgon, being 16 foute hie, did stande a holly bushe full of blacke birds and thrushis, which at the end of the musicke did singe and shake theire wynges. Divers other motions there was that the Grand Sinyor wondered at.*'—Ed.

We had a long talk and I told her of her uncle's—I should say her great-uncle's—theory of the elements.

'Men are never content to accept life as it is,' she said. 'For ever theorizing and trying to trim the universe to fit their own neat conceptions and absurd notions.' She continued for a while in this vein, growing more and more animated as she poured scorn and derision on male antics.

For the pleasure of hearing her talk I told her how well the doctor's theory adapted itself to the royal family. At my mention of Gertrude she drew away and, with that sudden change of mood which is all Penelope, asked whether the rumours now current at court had yet penetrated to my ivory tower. Sensing an enjoyable scandal, I prayed her to say on.

'You will not relish it,' she said. 'But perhaps it is better that you hear it from me than from some *adulterate* source.'

'What is all this?' I asked.

'Believe it or not, Claudius, but it is put about that Gertrude is your mistress.'

I was dumbfounded.

Her mood changed again, and I looked at her in bewilderment as her laughter pealed around the room; she became almost inarticulate with mirth.

'I don't find that this cripples me with merriment,' I said stiffly. This set her off again.

'Oh, Claudius. You, the fastidious, and *inconsequent* Gertrude, and your face when I told you; it is really too much.'

'So it is indeed,' I said.

After a while she calmed herself, but not before she had all but flounced down on the grapes. I felt a trifle less morose after I had narrowly averted this disaster. Then we had another long talk and I was gratified to learn that she is of the same opinion as myself: that Gertrude is a good, kind, errant, amiable creature. I told her I should ignore this canard.

'Do not ignore it, Claudius. Despise it, yes; but be wary of it.'

I felt my gorge rise at all this implied of walking delicately amongst the tale-bearers and pimps of the palace. I shrugged in vexation.

'Please, Claudius.'

'Very well; of course you are right; I cannot but despise it; I shall contrive as best I may to be wary of it.'

I reminded her that the patient had been ordered to rest.

"There was something amiss with the prescription, after all, malingerer,' said she; and, popping two grapes in my mouth and one in hers, she slipped away.

15th April

More dead than alive after yesterday's rituals, notably the accession anniversary State banquet, which I overheard my nephew Hamlet describe, in a quaintly characteristic phrase, as 'a heavy-headed revel'. I would say, rather, 'heavy-stomached', for on these occasions of full ceremonial we must perforce endure at least twelve main courses; fewer than this would be an insult to the guests and—worse—a mortal insult to the palace chef and his army of scullions. I would set down the bill of fare here were it not that my vitals revolt at the recollection of so many ill-chafed dishes. It is deplorable that the banqueting hall is at such a distance from the kitchens that the grease congeals in transit through the draughty corridors.

As is customary, there was a guest of honour. But seldom can our Danish court functions have been enriched by one of such towering stature and ebony magnificence as His Highness the Crown Prince of Ethiopia, heir-apparent to the Lion of Judah; his flowing robes of scarlet and silver, flashing rings of emerald, ruby and sapphire, soft gold twisted bracelets and nodding plumes seemed to extinguish all other colour from the great dining hall and to tarnish the heavy, chased palace gold plate.

Such guests are always a problem, unversed as they are in our protocol and table conventions. On this occasion all passed off well except for one awkward moment when the royal giant seized a sweetmeat from the silver dish before him and swallowed it whole, complete with its protective covering of lead foil. Down his vast gullet it went, like a stone to a bottomless well. A spasm passed through me; but hastily composing myself I deftly offered the dish to my neighbour on the right, who passed it silently behind him to a discreet footman.

This incident had passed unobserved by most, but not by my wretched nephew, sitting opposite. A hush falling upon the company about the same time, he was heard to remark, in a conspiratorial tone fit to span the Skagerrak, that 'every cloud has a silver lining'. I hastily engaged our oriental friend in a tedious discussion of the Hamitic Semites in Ethiopia. It is fortunate that his acquaintance with the Danish tongue is small; we managed pretty well in an uncouth version of classical Latin.

CHAPTER FOUR

21st April

Disaster! Voltimand has been trapped by the King's espionage group working on the frontier in the guise of customs officials. His fate is unknown, for my faithful Sigismund could trail him no farther lest he should suffer the same extremity. Worse still— I blush for the inhuman admission—the fate of my letter to old Norway is also unknown. What folly to suppose that safety resides in equivocation! It is more probable that my artificially contrived ambiguities will supply the casuists of the Advocate-General's department with extra material for the indictment.

I affected lack of interest in the news communicated to me by Sigismund, remarking in an unfeeling manner that Voltimand's misfortune was no more than an occupational hazard of his calling. I congratulated him on his own escape and scouted his suggestion that any further inquiry be made into the matter. Sigismund is not to be fooled by such bland talk; though he does not—I hope—know the purport of my message to old Norway, he cannot but perceive the importance of a mission which would otherwise have been entrusted to an expendable member of my intelligence staff. All this Sigismund knows—would that I did not know it too!

23rd April

How do greater troubles eclipse those of less moment! Today, in the absence of the King, who is away from the capital reviewing Crappswein's new-found mercenaries in North Zealand, I received a deputation headed by Polonius, ostensibly to discuss routine matters of State. With Polonius were four members of the Council, having nothing in common with each other, so far as I have any cause to know, except a marked reluctance to support the establishment. To describe them as dissidents would be extravagant, for our system admits of none, but such is their cast of mind. The four were—no, I shall not set down their names, not for any tenderness towards them; but towards the old man, who risks so much by this, I still feel a lively sense of obligation and affection.

For once Polonius paid no heed to the business in hand and remained silent in my audience chamber. As soon as the business was concluded, unusually early, I prepared to dismiss the ministers, thankful to be done with it so soon. This was the signal for Polonius to crave leave to speak. The burden of his address was disturbing. He declares that 'the whole nation' is solidly against the war with Norway, that it is a criminal folly, that it can lead to nothing but catastrophe whether we lose or win the war—subjugation if we lose, economic disaster if we win.

He stepped with Agag-like delicacy about the person of the King, but directed a diatribe at Crappswein. Yet, as every child in Denmark knows, the King is at one with his Commander-in-Chief in aspirations and martial ardour, so it was not hard for Polonius to bring both of them within the ambit of his invective.

After I had listened to this for some while I asked my customary question—what had anything of it to do with me? Polonius declares that since my speech to the Council it is common knowledge, even amongst those of the baser sort, that the Prince Claudius, and he only, can provide the focal point for an effective opposition.

'This is treason,' I said. (I seem to have said that before.)

There was a long and pregnant silence as I looked around the audience chamber at my five interlocutors. Polonius sat for once still, impassive, with a little smile flickering about his eyes as he looked me in the face, relaxed, waiting. The other four, less hardened to such crunches, sat restless with eyes averted, fiddling with gown or scroll. At last one of them—he shall remain anonymous—said: 'Your Highness, the time has come for plain speaking. This affair will be carried and he that is not with us is against us. Your Highness should understand that we have good reason to know that our sentiments are shared by Your Highness and of that we have *ample and demonstrable proof*.'

'I thank you all', I said, addressing myself to Polonius, 'for bringing to my attention a matter which it is most evident is apt for me, in the paramount interest of the welfare and safety of the State of Denmark, to communicate in person and in privacy to my brother the King, to whom we all owe and submit our continued and unwavering allegiance.' I paused for a moment for breath and inspiration and then added, a little lamely: '*All of which* I shall be pleased to submit to his deliberation and judgment on his return to the seat of government.'

After these flocculent remarks I abruptly terminated the uneasy session. Do they suppose that I shall report their treasonable activities to the King? Or that, being so far committed by the miscarriage of Voltimand, I shall accede to their request and lend myself to their designs? Equivocation, equivocation! They may know the answer to this—Polonius surely does?—but surely I do not.

24th April

In the King's absence I had thought it fitting to invite Gertrude and my nephew Hamlet to a modest supper party. This had been arranged some days since, and little did I think that I should receive my guests in such perturbation of spirit as has been thrust on me by intermediate events. I had thought also to distract Hamlet a little from his ill humours by asking Polonius to bring his daughter Ophelia, and my own by inviting Penelope, accompanied for propriety by her great-uncle Stavridos.

The evening went passably well, if exception be allowed for

the final incident. It is not every day that Gustav sets a table before the Queen—a far less exacting task, did he know it, than to satisfy the fastidious Penelope, for Gertrude, dear soul, will eat with relish anything that is set before her. One may doubt whether she recognizes such elementary distinctions of the gourmet as the eatable, the palatable and the delectable. Yet she keeps her milk-white complexion, stoked by an indiscriminate and massive diet of cakes, buns, cream, nuts and sweetmeats. Strange, too, how her limbs (not that one is privileged to see any large expanse of them) seem to glow with a faint shade of pink. 'Do you know something?' whispers Penelope with a conspiratorial air. 'She must be that tint all over.'

After supper little Ophelia sang to us in her true, dulcet voice. I could see that Penelope was not favourably impressed, particularly when Hamlet accompanied—or, more precisely, followed—her on his newly practised recorder. Stavridos, of course, being rather deaf, dozed happily; Polonius seemed wrapped in thought, as well he might be, a privilege denied to the host. Only Gertrude and I seemed to find the songs of any merit, and perhaps for the same reason, for we are both tenderly disposed towards the innocent and unassuming singer. I was enchanted by one little song:

> How should I your true love know
> From another one?
> By his cockle hat and staff
> And his sandal shoon.

And yet, I thought—dear heart, what do you know of the Prince Hamlet? How should you your true love know, indeed? He is no pilgrim, but for all that you may feel the staff.

Hamlet, I must own, was at his most charming—all pleasantries and no barbed quips. Yet there is something amiss with his relationship with Ophelia, something I suspect not wholesome. I find it hard to define: an occasional brusqueness, a domineering manner as though he stood—or would wish to stand—over her with a whip. Only a girl of her exceptional innocence and sweetness of disposition—for she has too much spirit to be docile—could tolerate this brutishness. It is as though he derived satisfaction from lashing the object of his affection.

I pray that Penelope is wrong when she predicts that this is but an image of things to come. She declares that it is buzzed about the court that there are certain deviations from the norm in Hamlet's sexual inclinations, of a recognizable pattern by no means pleasant to contemplate, and, with respect to Ophelia, horrible indeed.

I believe I could write a book about my nephew Hamlet. Yet how could I hope to capture that vivacity and charm, those mischievous cavortings with turns of phrase, those engaging flights of fancy? Or how reconcile them with his black moods, long spells of brooding melancholy and fits of savagery? It seems to me, sometimes, that there are two beings in one.

My guests departed at midnight, Hamlet as effusive in his thanks as Gertrude. He was the last to take his leave. Looking about him to be sure that we were unobserved, he withdrew from his doublet a letter and handed it to me, saying: 'Your servant, nuncle.' Then with a malicious grin (he knows how much these archaisms vex me), he departed after his mother. The letter is my own to Norway.

26th April

I confronted Sigismund with the letter. With some presence of mind he evolved a theory that the frontier guards must have sold the letter to an agent of Fortinbras and that he in turn had passed it to Hamlet. Sigismund is too discreet to suggest that Fortinbras and Hamlet have any common design, but he must suspect that I suspect it. 'Fortinbras is a trouble-maker both in and outside Norway,' was as far as he would go. But nothing is so simple in this tormented scene; it is treacherously facile to fit events to theory. Allowing that, in my belief, Fortinbras and Hamlet have made some compact, of which the drift and commitment are yet concealed, Fortinbras could surely make better use of this letter had it fallen into his hands. No—this is the work of my nephew Hamlet and of him alone. I hold that my small intelligence corps surpasses that of the King, but both must yield to Hamlet's.

27th April

Immediately after his return the King summoned me to audience. It is rare for us to discuss matters of State—more rare to sit, as we did today, for upwards of two hours together and without the distraction of counsellors.

I attended the summons in some uneasiness, supposing that word must have reached the King of my giving ear to the dissidents or—worse—that my nephew had revealed to him the purport of my letter to Norway. But all was well. The King was in high fettle. Crappswein's mercenaries, it seems, are good value for money—well trained, well disciplined and well equipped. (Whether they have stomach for the fight remains to be seen.) The King himself took the ceremonial parade and was in good voice. Martial evolutions were performed to perfection in obedience to the royal thunder of command. Had Crappswein not already achieved the highest rank known to the military hierarchy of Denmark, he would unquestionably be marked for promotion. I could see that in my brother's eyes the war is already won.

The main subject for discussion, as it turned out, was the regency during my brother's absence on the campaign, to which, it seems, he now deems himself irrevocably committed, though by what process of logic I am unable to discern. His notion was to appoint Gertrude, Hamlet and myself as a triumvirate with plenary powers. Plenary powers, indeed! I was obliged to point out that a nation at war cannot afford to wait upon the deliberations of a committee and that he must perforce treat the capital as his base headquarters; moreover, as I remarked, Hamlet would be absent at Wittenberg for much of the time and this alone made the proposal unworkable. I did not say—though it is sufficiently obvious—that the burden of government would in any case fall upon me, that Gertrude would be a drag and Hamlet, as ever, a thorn in the side. Thus I should be effectively hampered, but infallibly censured for every delay or miscarriage.

'The responsibility in war is too great for the Queen alone,' he said.

'Then let it be Hamlet,' I replied. 'He must relinquish his studies at Wittenberg for the duration of the campaign.'

'The Prince is too young and inexperienced,' he said. 'Moreover if he is not at Wittenberg the people will demand that he be at the war.'

And so it was settled that I act alone. We had an amiable

talk. I warned him that there were refractory elements in the nation, some in high places, opposed to his war policy. He looked at me quizzically. 'Ah, Claudius,' said he, 'we shall never make a soldier of you. But what matter? There are other soldiers. Why dissemble? When you speak of waverers, you speak of yourself. You fear the war. Leave the war to me. *Chacun à son goût.*'

He meant, I think, let the cobbler stick to his last, but no matter: he speaks like a soldier and the shaft went home. I stayed silent.

'But you are loyal, Claudius. You shall hold the fort of Elsinore and view the battle from afar.' He laughed uproariously over this.

He thinks I am loyal. Perhaps this also is true. Loyal to the State of Denmark. Not to the person of the King. No, nor yet to the Prince of Denmark.

28th April

An evening with Penelope. Once more she is fidgety and strained. Not long since I could shed cares in her company. Now as well enter the Council chamber! Thus is night made joint-labourer with the day; we are all sacrificed to this post-haste and romage in the land.

Penelope declares that I am to be assassinated! I assured her that I cannot claim to be of such unenviable value to Denmark as to merit the attention. Alternatively—invoking my rusty skill of lawyer's pleading, which permits the juxta-position of ill-matched pleas—that I am as ready for it now as ever I was, since this is the lot of princes of the blood, to which they are trained from the cradle.

Penelope is maddeningly inconsequent and vague. She knows I am to be assassinated, but by whom, on what account, by what means or when, she does not know. The astrologers, it seems, take a concordantly dismal view of my horoscope at the present season. So be it—woman's stuff.

'Who would wish to assassinate me?', I inquired.

'Prince Hamlet, for one,' she replied. 'You stand between him and the throne; or if you do not, he thinks you do. This decision of the King's to prefer you in the regency—if it was the King's decision, I wonder . . .'

'It was the King's command,' I said. 'With some little assistance in arriving at a decision.'

'You were born to dig your own grave, Claudius. No matter, but it will not endear you to your nephew.'

'Let him endear himself to me,' I said, touched on the raw. 'Well, allowing that my nephew may think ill of his uncle, who else?'

'Whom the gods resolve to destroy they first make mad,' said she. 'You must be for the King or against him. What folly to listen to treason but remain silent! If it should come to the King's ears, what then?'

'Well, at least it would be assassination by due process of law,' I said sombrely.

'And if your friends miscarry?'

'With one exception they are not my friends. Nor am I privy to their designs. I am as uncertain of them as they are of me. They fear disclosure to the King.'

'I pray you may be right in that. But suppose they carry out their designs, as you call them. What recompense then for the Prince Claudius who would not join the faction?'

'Do you think *they* will assassinate me too?' I said. 'Are you not forgetting that I have only one life?'

She complains that I am ridiculing my own assassination, and that this is in poor taste. Quite the reverse: I find the prospect unappealing. But I must own to a perverse pleasure in contemplating the unfamiliar image of a Prince Claudius in this new guise—of such importance alive that he would be better seen dead. This is novelty indeed.

30th April

Again I am summoned to the King, in session in the inner Council chamber—a strange family council of his own devising. Also present were Polonius and the Lord Chief Justice, Grunwald. By a merciful providence the egregious Crappswein is detained in North Zealand on his military duties.

The King in his blunt manner announced his resolve to cross the frontier on the fifteenth of May at the head of his army. The campaign is to be concluded in three months. There will be victory celebrations in Christiania early in

August and he will return to Elsinore on the first day of
September.

'The very day on which partridge shooting begins,' inter-
jected my nephew Hamlet, looking slyly at me. I could sense
that he was in one of his devilish moods.

'That is enough,' said my brother, who does not care to be
interrupted and has no relish for his son's niceties of innuendo.
'I have resolved', he said, 'to entrust the regency to my brother
Claudius. The Prince will be answerable for the State of
Denmark for the duration of the campaign.'

'To whom will my uncle be answerable?' inquired my
nephew.

There were many possible answers to this piece of effrontery.
I cannot but applaud my brother's downright and stark reply.

'To me,' he said.

'So long as he is not answerable to his own conscience,'
murmured Hamlet. I affected not to hear.

At this point Gertrude turned to the King, and to everyone's
amazement said: 'And to whom will the Prince Claudius be
answerable if by ill fate or miscarriage of the event Your
Majesty should not return from the war to reign over Denmark?'

That is a question which has perturbed many minds overlong,
yet none but the ingenuous Gertrude would venture to put it
to the King in the publicity of the Council chamber. But the
King merely laughed loudly—he never laughs otherwise—and
patted her hand as one soothing a child frightened of the dark.

'Never fear, dear Gertrude,' he said. Then, looking at me, and
laughing again, 'Leave the war to me. Claudius will look
after you.'

It was Hamlet's turn to look sombre. Remembering the
absurd canard repeated to me by Penelope, I was hard put to
it to conceal amusement at this uxoriously solicitous utterance.
Happily Polonius stepped into the breach and quickly pursued
the advantage offered to him by Gertrude's opening of a subject
hitherto treated as unmentionable. He was saying that Her
Majesty's question was of vital importance to the State of
Denmark. Would the King permit the Lord Chief Justice to
refresh Her Majesty's recollection of the law and practice of
the Danish succession?

The subject was evidently not much to the King's liking, but he permitted Grunwald to proceed. In his heavy-jowled and ponderous manner, Grunwald expounded the electoral system, looking first at the Queen, then at the King, never at my nephew or myself.

When he had finished I said: 'There is one point on which the Lord Chief Justice will correct me if I am in error. Is it not accepted in our constitution that the electoral process, though theoretically paramount, is in practice but a ratification of the choice of the late reigning monarch?'

'That is so,' said Grunwald. 'The monarch's choice may in theory be accepted or rejected. Seldom is it rejected, yet it must be self-evident that it is the safety of the State that is paramount in all things.'

My nephew Hamlet and I both appeared to derive equal solace from this pronouncement of an elementary truth, as familiar to both of us as the backs of our own hands.

We passed on to other business.

10th May

A gap in my diary. Can it be that only the vexed in spirit keep journals? Is it possible to conceive of my brother doing so? Or Penelope? His diary would be empty, hers bursting at the seams and spilling over.

For ten days—let us be factual, consecutive, unvarnished— we have escaped the court. No touch of intrigue, no machinations, no dwelling at night on the miscarriage of plans and spies. Ten days at my country house, divorced from Gustav and the burnt offerings of his scullions, thank God also from the conscientious van Loon and his files and pedantry.

My caretaker Sussi seemed overjoyed to see me. 'So rare', she declares, 'are these visits for which we endure the long winter and these sad dust-sheets over all the furniture, always waiting, hoping. . . .'

I tell her she is a poetess of no mean merit, that soon she will recognize her true vocation and abandon my service for the meretricious tributes of long-haired young men in Elsinore. She laughs with gay abandon, her ample and uncorseted breasts shaking, and declares her undying devotion to my person and cuisine. What she says is true, not only of herself but of her husband Pieter—a faithful pair, simple, unspoilt and loyal.

All has been halcyon. Penelope here too, accompanied for propriety by her great-uncle. She and Sussi are thick as thieves. Their gales of laughter penetrate even the old man's dimming ears, and he turns to me with a quizzical look of conspiratorial sympathy. No word passes between us. I say to him, though the words are unspoken, that I can overhear Sussi, my peasant caretaker, whose vitality would reach to the moon. He replies by cocking an eyebrow (that notable feature) that the case is indistinguishable from that of his great-niece. They get along famously; so do we, and each of us with the others.

The sun shines every day from a cloudless sky. Can it be that there is such a place as Elsinore? Pieter has filled the flower-beds, trimmed the hedges. There is a blaze of early helianthemum; the blooms fall every evening, yet in the morning they are ablaze again—it is a daily miracle. Pieter takes me round the gardens, mortified that I missed the best of the tulips, zealous that I should prolong my stay for the early roses. Already the bees are humming at their work. I brace myself to the thought that in five days' time the King will cross the frontier and I must return to take over the government of Denmark.

The old man retires early, sleeps little and wakes early. Penelope and I talk far into the night and Sussi brings us hot chocolate and little croissants with home-made honey when the sun is already high, chiding us for lethargy which she attributes (not always justly) to excessive tributes to Venus. 'To the unmarried', Sussi says, 'the night is dark.' This observation, daily repeated and diversely construed, causes much mirth both to her and Penelope. The double joke is that Penelope must have taught it to Sussi. I reply feebly that according to Germanic legend all cats are grey in the dark. Penelope affects to be offended, Sussi to be outraged. Thus do we amuse ourselves.

For ten days I have cast off the Prince Claudius, providence be thanked.

II

Gertrude

CHAPTER FIVE

Undated

The King is dead. I write three days after the event, and at Elsinore. All is confusion; rumour and speculation are rife. Gertrude is distraught; Hamlet, on the instant recalled from Wittenberg, broods sullenly. Polonius smothers all in rhetoric. Stavridos is back; his report . . . (*illegible*) How to prevent disorders . . . time short . . .

> [The manuscript at this point defies interpretation. The entries reveal a marked deterioration of calligraphy and much of the text has been scored through and interlineated. Also two pages of the folio have been torn out—whether by the hand of Claudius or another it is impossible to judge.—*Ed.*]

5th June

Denmark laid to rest. The crowds sullen; so also—worse—the royal bodyguard. Crappswein must go. But first consolidate: *fortiter in re, suaviter in modo.*

How came it? Poisoned, not a doubt. Stavridos, who has made a study of recondite criminology, swears to the deadly

49

juice of the common yew, or hebona, poured in the porches of the ears.

None knows of this diagnosis (if it can be so described) except Stavridos himself, his deputy Staab, who was called to the corpse, and I. None, that is, but the assassin, his principals and his accomplices.

Oh, horrible! Dispatched whilst sleeping in his orchard of a hot summer's afternoon—his wont, as I well know, for thereby his great frame would draw refreshment and momentum to carry it into the small hours, to the chagrin and fatigue of his court.

Few know how the King died, yet how many suspect?

7th June

All still in flux. Hamlet dour, Gertrude ever inconsolable. Polonius more prodigal of words than thought.

By tradition the chief ministers of State assembled today to appoint the date of the election and vote measures for interim government. When the succession is obvious this is no more than a formality. This was not such an occasion. I was careful to ensure that my nephew Hamlet and I were both present and that neither of us presided. With a gesture of good grace my nephew, deferring to my years, conceded me the chair at the foot of the Council table, seating himself at my right hand. He knows well how to make a show of humility when it will serve an end; as the French say, *reculer pour mieux sauter*.

Thus did I face my late brother's vacant, heavy, high-canopied chair at the extremity of the table. Can it be that I feel the tension of these sleepless nights and fevered times? It seemed that my brother sat as of old in his accustomed place. The dark shadows coalesced imperceptibly into the heaving movement of his large-knit frame and from their depths I heard the familiar, harsh and grating tones of my brother's voice speaking words of no comfort: 'Now you, so wont to know better than I, ever despising my bluntness, taste for yourselves the torments of indecision; bear you now the heavy burden of vacillation and divided counsels.'

Then there was a confusion of sounds, which marched and counter-marched as in a parade-ground evolution, falling at last into a pattern of hollow laughter—the loud and rumbustious laughter of my brother in the flesh. Then the voice resumed, insistent, inescapable: 'The King is dead, long live the King.'

By an immense effort of will I collected myself and gazed steadfastly towards the head of the table. The ornately carved chair of State, emblazoned with the royal arms, was unquestionably void of all but shadows. Yet a moment later, as I turned with feigned attention to the pontifications of Grunwald, my spirit congealed to ice.

It was not the voice of Grunwald that I heard, but another—thick, toneless, vibrant, familiar. 'Ah, never fear, dear Gertrude. Leave the war to me. Claudius will look after you.' Then the laugh again, more resonant, more maniacal:

'But you are loyal, Claudius. You shall hold the fort of Elsinore and view the battle from afar.'

I turned my head a little towards my nephew Hamlet. In moments of great stress there is a communion of spirit between us that I cannot in all justice deny. He rose from his place and plucked Grunwald by the gown. 'Look to the Prince Claudius!' he exclaimed. I do not know what else; they tell me I fainted.

Later I found myself in the west antechamber, Hamlet solicitous at my side. 'The time is out of joint,' he said.

The Council was adjourned for an hour. By my order and pending the election, the late King's chair of State has been shrouded out of respect for his memory—or so I have given it out—and has been placed under close guard for the nonce. This done, I adjured my nephew to take his place at the head of the table, which he did after the manner of one not needful of guidance in such matters.

But the resolutions of the Council may have been less to his liking. Preparations for the war are to continue, but the opening of the campaign is postponed *sine die*. And pending the election, appointed for a month hence, I am confirmed in the regency by the late King's own choice. As is so often true of vital decisions taken by the Council, one would be at a loss to substantiate them on any logical grounds; they represent a consensus of inclination rather than a reasoned conclusion. No matter—I am confirmed in the regency and all ministers are confirmed in their appointments. In the interim, pending the election, they are answerable to me.

E

10th June

There have been times—I shall not try to conceal it—when I could have wished—when indeed I *did* wish—my brother Hamlet dead. His grossness, his crassness, his so stupid glints and gleams of crude peasant cunning, his thunderbolts of command issuing from an impregnable fortress of unreasoning infallibility—and, yes, I must own it, the high and crescent affection (hard words to write) in which he was held by his subjects throughout his long reign: these were as a boil in the armpit to such a pedant and sceptic as I.

Yet now it is my dearest wish that my brother reigned once more! Disorders multiply. The mob, ignorant or impatient of the electoral processes by law established, have twice in ugly mood gathered at the palace gates. There has been much loose talk and vapid comment. On the first occasion Hamlet presented himself on the balcony—needlessly, in my opinion, certainly prematurely but not unsuccessfully; he was advised, he declares, that the mob were baying for him and he wished to avoid bloodshed of the palace guard. At all events his popularity commanded silence, and with a discretion beyond his years he made light of the occasion, humoured the crowd and persuaded them to go about their business.

The second of these events cannot be dismissed so lightly. In the first place it is clear from intelligence reports that it was no casual gathering of the idle or dissident, but at the core of the mob was a well-disciplined claque of Hamlet's own sycophants; on the fringe, need it be said, the loud-mouthed demonstrators which any party with a supposititious grievance may muster at will. Secondly the rout soon became a riot and worse, for Hamlet had reckoned without any opposition. The militant Laertes, now returned from Paris, had evidently been apprised of this impending clamour, doubtless calculated to bring Hamlet to the palace balcony again (does Hamlet yet emulate the great Julius and think to decline the crown thrice?) [1]

[1] An old tradition. *Cf.* Shakespeare's *Julius Caesar*, Act I, Sc. 2. *Per* Casca: 'And then he offered it a third time; he put it a third time by; and still as he refused it the rabblement shouted and clapped their chapped hands, and threw up their sweaty night-caps, and uttered such a deal of stinking breath because Caesar refused the crown, that it had almost choked Caesar . . . and for my own part I durst not laugh, for fear of opening my lips and receiving the bad air.'—*Ed.*

The upshot of this: the Primrose League were surprised from the rear and on two flanks. There has been—alas—much butchery.

All this bodes ill for the State of Denmark, yet the past hangs over me with a more malign influence than the future. It is whispered that I, the King's own brother, have murdered the King. There have been attempts to conceal this scurrilous talk from me, yet I have it from those most loyal—from Sigismund, from Stavridos, even from Bartholomew (now translated from the palace library to be curator of my records—the sole constructive act of my short-lived regency). That I was at a great distance from the crime, incommunicado on my private estate at the time, counts for naught. The presence of Stavridos with me is judged a sinister feature. If poison is afoot, obviously the first step is to kidnap the Court physician! Such, I gather, is the *ratio decidendi* of the case.

Yet it is enough for me to be accused by unknown and malicious or ill-informed persons of such a crime as to twist my conscience in an agony of self-searching. Is there not some truth in it? What of the caucus which warned me in plain terms that Hamlet's war policy was not to be suffered? What greater impulse could I have given to men already desperate than to talk of treason and hint at disclosure? These are heavy thoughts. *Qui facit per alium facit per se.* A brother's murder—it has the primal eldest curse upon it.

12th June

I sent for Polonius, thinking to acquaint myself more nearly with the true causes of the late street rioting, and in particular with the factious policy of his son. I warned him that the resounding scandal to the household and office of Polonius himself and his long and loyal service to the Crown had alone restrained me from exerting myself against Laertes on account of the late disturbances. He accepted the rebuke without rancour and in the exact degree of deference due to my most impermanent office of regent, no more. He has an astonishing facility for returning a rebuff with compound interest.

'What then is this quarrel with the Prince Hamlet?' I inquired, with a naïveté which ill becomes me. The question could hardly have been put in a less pointed manner; I have no wish to offend the old man.

I had expected some tale of Hamlet's suspected intrigues with the Prince Fortinbras, but surprisingly Polonius declares that this is but a small part of the case against my nephew.

'To speak plainly,' he said (not to be tedious, I abridge his comments), 'their policy is to ensure a settled and stable government.'

'Who are *they*?'

He reminded me that I had inquired about the policy of the party of Laertes.

'To speak plainly,' he said again, 'the Prince Hamlet's temperament is unsuited to government. To govern one must be governable.'

'A remarkable proposition,' I replied. 'And hardly true', I added, 'of his late father.'

'Ah, there you have it,' said Polonius.

I was struck dumb by the formidable implications of this reply. At length I rejoined:

'You are saying this was a political murder?'

'That is so. But let it be said that the regicides—whoever they may be—were determined to ensure above all things the safety of the State. That was their motive and it is still their objective.'

'You are well acquainted with the motives of the regicides?'

He remained silent and after a while I continued:

'Could it be that they were also concerned to save their own necks?'

He bowed his head in assumed deference to my percipience. 'It is no calumny that I serve the interests of the State,' he replied.

'Then what is your policy? What advantage to the State in this senseless opposition to the Prince? These daily disorders are the negation of policy.'

It seems that his policy is to persuade the electoral college—that antiquated asylum of fuddy-duddies—to overlook the obvious claims of Hamlet to his father's throne. Polonius declares that there can be but one other choice. It is not Gertrude.

I undertook to give the matter thought.

13th June

Interminable and inconclusive reflections upon the State of Denmark:

1. Hamlet has the will to govern, but not the temperament; I have the temperament but not the will.
2. Hamlet is the idol of the mob; their dislike of me is matched only by my own detestation of them.
3. Hamlet's capacity for wrecking the State by ill-considered and precipitate action far exceeds my own, operating by distrust and indecision.
4. We are equal in inexperience of government; he may learn (though what?), yet I doubt that I shall.
5. Polonius and Laertes together exert a great influence in my favour, but the Primrose League are the more vociferous. Polonius is at the end of his term. Laertes is too downright, lacks subtlety, rides for a fall. Neither is a match for Hamlet.
6. Why burden myself with an unwelcome sovereignty, equally detestable to my own inclinations and my nephew's ambitions? But what if he reigns? As I have heard him sometimes proclaim in a cant phrase: *Ay, there's the rub.*
7. What of the murder? What is the choice of princes of the blood?—not whether to be assassinated, but by whom and when: a choice of evils, as is this whole mortal coil.

From such nice balancing of the imponderable there can but be one escape—to music or mathematics. Thirty-seven votes in the electoral college. Of these sixteen infallibly Hamlet's, nine almost certainly mine. Assume an equal split of the residual twelve: his twenty-two, mine fifteen. Split three to him and nine to me: he yet overtops me by one. What a fantasy!

CHAPTER SIX

15th June

Today a long audience of the Queen, at her own wish. By
courtesy she is yet known as the Queen, for to name her the
Queen Mother would be to prejudge the election.

I begin to ask myself if I have been greatly mistaken in her.
Did I say that she dotes upon Hamlet? True, yet it seems that
she shares with Ophelia, and it may be for a kindred cause,
a love underlaid with fear—perhaps an unspoken bond between
them? I sense in all that Gertrude says of Hamlet a shrinking
from him. Is it apprehension for him or for herself? I should
say for both: an instinctive knowledge of the destructive nature
of their relationship. This may in some small degree serve to
explain the strange trend of Gertrude's thoughts—emotions,
rather—concerning the succession. *Gertrude fears Hamlet's
succession.*

What does she fear? How could I hope to analyse irrational
emotions, but dimly understood and half rejected by herself?
She is oppressed by a mountain of fears. Some indeed are
reasonable enough: Hamlet is wayward, will make enemies;

his popularity with the mob may turn to hatred all too soon when his youthful pranks and caprices find grosser shape in new-found opportunity for misrule. But underlying all this is an obsessive fear that he will be assassinated, as his father has been. I have to remind myself that Gertrude, a margrave's daughter, no more, and as much a foreigner as Penelope, was not schooled to assassination, as were we of the blood royal. For how many years has she lived under the shadow of it, perhaps made all the more menacing by the late King's temperament, so indifferent to this commonplace of monarchy?

And yet, though these fears predominate, I seem to detect—do I do her an injustice?—a less creditable motive which she would doubtless disown. Gertrude has long been Queen of Denmark. The empty ceremonial of sovereignty, the salutes of cannon, the glitter of State banquets, gracious and choice words fitly spoken by the first lady of the land, heavy brocades, satins and jewels to set off her ample figure, the ladies of her bed-chamber and her train of attendants—all these are as the breath of life to Gertrude. Is it all to be relinquished for a dower house? In Gertrude's eyes, still red from weeping over my brother's bier, I perceive another fear: a fear of this new oppressive title with all that it implies of faded charms and banishment to a drear obscurity reserved for the widow and relict.

Seeking to test her, I announced it as my resolve—in fact as yet indeterminate—to return to a private station so soon as the electoral college have had done with the formality of pro-nouncing for Hamlet as successor to his father's throne. She recoiled breathlessly from the proposal and implored me to submit myself to the better judgment of Polonius. 'To what purpose?' I asked. Such a course could but deepen the chasm between the rival factions of Hamlet and Laertes, to the injury of the State. Moreover on any showing Hamlet would carry a clear majority in the electoral college.

Gertrude's ignorance of State affairs is so profound that one bumps with astonishment upon a bottom of native common sense. 'Do not allow yourself to forget, dear Claudius,' said she, 'that the Queen also may exert influence within the electoral college. Moreover there are waverers to whom it only needs to be said that the Queen speaks also in the name of the late King.'

I was deeply shocked and, craving time for deliberation, I took my leave in no easy frame of mind. I had come to console a distraught sister-in-law. It seems that I have been conversing with a politician.

16th June

When tormented by one woman, consult another. The cure will be worse than the disease, but what of that? It is a commonplace of nature; Stavridos himself would not deny it.

I will allow that Penelope is a good listener. She heard me out and, since I am endowed—some would say, cursed—with an accurate memory, she was perforce obliged to endure a complete and verbatim account of my exchanges with the Queen. I had supposed that this narrative would astonish her. Not so. At last she said:

'Well, what could you expect?'

'Certainly not this,' I replied. 'The Queen has ever favoured and sustained Hamlet, even against his own father. It could hardly be supposed that she would now wish to obstruct him in the succession.'

'You do not understand women,' replied Penelope shortly.

'That is becoming increasingly evident,' I said.

As a matter of fact, this is about the last thing I would admit to. I rather fancy that I *do* understand women. My remark was, needless to say, sardonic. For some reason, obscure to me, Penelope seemed to think it amusing; she has an inscrutable sense of humour.

'You do not seem to be greatly surprised by my news,' I remarked after a while. I confess I felt a little irked by her reception of what, to me, was a cataclysm of nature.

'Of course not. I told you years ago that it was predestined that you would reign.'

'Some astrologer's stuff!' I cried, out of countenance with this at a time of imperative crisis.

It was her turn to look sombre.

'And I was to be assassinated,' I added, not content to leave well alone.

'Both,' said she.

I remarked that I begin to feel more and more like my namesake Claudius—I refer, of course, to Tiberius Claudius Drusus Nero Germanicus, who by all accounts was invested with the purple on the death of Caligula. I deplored the loss of those four books of Tacitus and part of another, for doubtless in this lost text the master described this event in his customary pithy style.

Penelope was amused by the analogy, but declared it to be false. 'For one thing,' she said, 'Claudius was created emperor by popular acclaim of the legions; there is no comparison there. And it is hardly in perspective to equate the late King with Caligula.'

'Very true,' I said; 'but Claudius was none the less a philosopher and scholar. It may be doubted whether history has done him justice. Consider, for example, the port of Ostia . . .'

'But it may be that history has done full justice to Messalina,' she interposed, with one of her rapid flights of imagination. 'Now there is a comparison for you.'

We amused ourselves for a while upon this preposterous comparison between the inoffensive Gertrude and Messalina, of whom Tacitus remarked that she grew weary of the very facility of her adulteries. Her spurious marriage to the egregious Silius in the emperor's lifetime—a story so well attested—yet strains credulity to the limit.

'Do you remember', said I, with my fatal memory for the exact text, 'how Tacitus described it?' And I repeated that remarkable line, how Messalina 'craved the name of wife for the sake of the monstrous infamy, that last source of delight for the reckless'.

'Well, that may be,' said Penelope; 'but to my thinking it does no more than reveal that Tacitus was ignorant of women. It was not, as he suggests, that Messalina derived pleasure from being more amoral. That is typical of a man's view. It was simply that she had exhausted all other excitements but one—to defy the emperor in full view of the patricians of Rome.'

'Well,' said I, with the unworthy satisfaction of invoking a feminine argument, 'she sadly misjudged the emperor and met her deserts.'

I should have been content to continue this discussion of the depravities of Messalina, but Penelope remorselessly turned the conversation back to the present day, revealing that she had herself been closeted with the Queen; thus it was that she had been forewarned of my own audience.

Even now I may doubt that the half has been told me. Yet the half that is told is enough in all conscience. Penelope declares that it is the Queen's purpose to offer me her hand in marriage. By the Queen's command she is bidden to disclose this to me in confidence that I may transmit the reply before she commits herself in a more formal manner.

The Queen's method of communicating this extraordinary message astounded and angered me. I guessed—wrongly—that Penelope could but be the victim of the Queen's stupidity or will to wound. I expressed myself with vehemence.

'No, no!', Penelope broke in. 'Please do not torment yourself. You must try to understand the Queen. I know you think her vain, vapid, tactless; and so she is, but to her friends she is kind, considerate and tender. Never was she more considerate than in this. She asked me to be the bearer of this message because she said . . .'

It is rare for Penelope to be incoherent.

'Well, what did she say?' I could not master my ill temper.

'She said she knew I love you, Claudius. God knows I do. And that she would not stand between us, except that I consent.'

'Well?' I said.

'There is no help for it, Claudius. The Queen is right. Your safety and hers depend on it. You must marry the Queen. Together you may crush your enemies.'

'It is true that there is the safety of Denmark to be considered,' I said.

'Oh,' she cried in exasperation, 'would that I had never set eyes on Denmark! To the devil with Denmark, and with Hamlet too!'

She felt better after this. I consoled her as best I might, though a thousand thoughts were churning my brain to curds. I dared not ask how much of this plot was of the Queen's devising and how much was her own. It is true, though, that the Queen has a great regard for Penelope and Penelope for the Queen. Here is something pleasant to contemplate in the present state of Denmark.

With a heavy heart I gave an affirmative reply.

17th June

No sooner had I returned to my own apartments than I was struck by a thought with the impact of a thunderbolt. I sat down at once and composed a cryptic message to Penelope in coded Latin, instructing the messenger to return with the reply. Within the hour I received it—a quotation from Ovid, as unhelpful as it is familiar:

> Claudius,
> I implore you, more discretion.
> *Qui finem quaeris amoris,*
> *Credit amor rebus; res age, tutus eris.*[1]
> Penelope.

It is untrue that I seek an end of love; what I seek is escape from its beginning.

18th June

The Queen's hand formally accepted. Penelope is right; we shall do very well. It would not be fitting that I set down here all the trivia of this occasion. Gertrude contrived the matter to perfection, with a little sentiment, but none too much; there was no regal condescension, in fact she contained her tears with difficulty. Weeping women are my cross; they look so very plain when they weep—it is hard to resist them.

19th June

A long session, all too tedious: the Queen, Polonius and I. Is it preferable to announce the nuptials before the electoral vote, which is to be taken in ten days' time? Or afterwards? Should we apprise only the electoral college, and if so when? How long will it take for the betrothal to become the talk of every pot-house? If we leave it too late, those slow-witted burghers

---

[1] You who seek an end of love [remember that] love yields to affairs; be busy and you will be safe.

(some of them already in their dotage) will not have time to turn over in bed, let alone change their thinking and suffrage. Yet, if we tell them too soon, we risk organized opposition by Hamlet, further discords and rioting and justifiable complaints of rigging the election.

All this is anathema. The decision having been taken, I should announce it forthwith and in no uncertain manner. Already in two days—can it be so short a time?—I feel myself King of Denmark. I am no longer the Prince Claudius. None know of this but I; only Penelope, the Queen and Polonius have the knowledge to suspect it and only Penelope has the wit, God bless her.

There swelled in my heart, eclipsing all this commerce of ways and means, a great pæan of praise that I am now both master and servant of Denmark; and I framed it in my mind so:

> No jocund health that Denmark drinks today,
> But the great cannon to the clouds shall tell,
> And the King's rouse the heavens shall bruit again,
> Re-speaking earthly thunder.

No matter that I cannot fatigue myself with these nice calculations. Polonius at least is rejuvenated. Like the scriptural charger of old, he scents the battle from afar. A word here, a word there, all to be timed to perfection, a soufflé served on time—and that too is mostly hot air—well, in truth, we may safely leave it to him: in such matters he is a sure guide. He concedes that the result of the election will not be approved by the mob, but he asks what one expects of a cold bath: a sense of exhilaration (instant announcement of the Queen's betrothal is apparently to provide this). So it is decided that the announcement is to follow hard upon.

Polonius declares, in a phrase that he is apt to crack the wind of, that if he proves wrong in his predictions, he is to be no assistant for the State 'but keep a farm and carters'. In this he speaks more truly than he knows, but the time is not yet.

CHAPTER SEVEN

27th June

Of the thirty-seven votes, twenty-one cast for me, sixteen for
Hamlet. No abstentions. A clear majority of five. The ballot
is reputedly secret, but I have it on the best authority that three
of the original sixteen voters that I predicted for my nephew
shifted their allegiance; yet he made good the loss as to two
from the waverers and one from the ranks of my own faithful.
The Queen's influence has been paramount in the election:
Polonius deserves all credit for making it effective; he is the
master of canvassers.

[We may infer that one lunar month or thereabouts was the
term of the regency. Claudius understandably failed to note the
exact date of his brother's death, but he first wrote in his diary
'three days after the event' and gives the date of the State
obsequies in a later entry (5th June). It seems likely that about
a week would have elapsed (allowing for the autopsy) in
preparation for so unexpected a State funeral, with its elaborate
ceremonial. This would set the King's death at about 29th May.
This may seem early in the year for his sleeping in the orchard
'of a hot summer's afternoon' (entry of 5th June); more so

63

for the 'heat wave' noted in the entry of 10th May. But it should be remembered that the Julian and first Gregorian calendars were inaccurate. It is for this reason—as anglers on the Test and Itchen well know—that the so-called '*may*-fly' has retained its name, though it rarely appears on the chalk-streams of England before June.—*Ed.*]

28th June

Civil marriage with Gertrude. The ceremonial wedding to follow and to be combined with the coronation: a nice problem for that feather-brained mountebank, young Osric (master of ceremonies), who has now to set his modest talents to the problem of concerting precedence, time and space.

Eventually I sanctioned—and incidentally initiated—a plan of escape from his dilemma; otherwise how contrive that the octogenarian margrave Shinck could at one and the same time be handing the King the golden ewer (symbolic of purification of sin) and supervising the descension of the Queen from the No. 2 State coach? The solution is simple—coronation first, wedding ceremony immediately afterwards. There will be some shuffling about as the aged senators exchange robes and places (some of them do turn and turn about at weddings and coronations) but, as I said to Osric, ceremonial occasions are always a feast or a famine.

There are numerous advantages in this procedure: (1) economy of effort and saving of expense to the public funds, and we are much over-stretched by the late King's military zeal; (2) avoiding the anticlimax of a second great State occasion soon after the first (to say nothing of the funeral)—the mob are soon replete; (3) royalty on such occasions are sitting fowl—as vulnerable as a halberdier recruit on the skyline—and the price of survival is really too high; (4) (not least), we have work to do, both Gertrude and I.

Ah, Gertrude and I! We have privately compacted—at my suggestion—that though in law we are husband and wife from this day, we shall better avoid all breath of scandal if we con-tinue to occupy our separate apartments in the palace until after the public ceremony. For this relief much thanks.

[The purpose of this civil ceremony is hard to understand, unless it was required by law or was intended to consolidate the ranks of the 'waverers'. As with much else entered in Claudius's diary, one is left confused and irritated. The civil marriage evidently took place almost exactly a month after the death of the late King. As will be seen, the coronation and State wedding, a combined ceremony, took place yet a fortnight later. The more credit for accuracy to William Shakespeare: *vide* Hamlet's speech in Act 1, Sc. 2, line 138, 'but two months dead, nay not so much, not two' (consistent with the date of this famous soliloquy)—but see lines 146–51:

> Let me not think on 't: Frailty, thy name is woman!
> A little month [*civil marriage*]; or ere those shoes were old
> With which she follow'd my poor father's body,
> Like Niobe, all tears, why she . . .
> . . . married with mine uncle.

The chronology may be deduced thus:

(*i*) From King Hamlet's death to the civil marriage, one month;

(*ii*) From the civil marriage to the State ceremony, about two weeks;

(*iii*) From the State ceremony to the Council of State and soliloquy, about another two weeks (*infra*).

If this calendar is examined it will be seen that Hamlet was accurate enough. 'But two months dead, nay not so much, not two' would be the gap from his father's death to the date of speaking the soliloquy. 'A little month' would cover the short stretch from the funeral to the civil ceremony, a mere three weeks and two days.—*Ed.*]

6th July

More than a week has elapsed since the election—long enough for me to take certain precautionary measures. These indeed have so fully occupied my time and thoughts that I have sadly neglected my journal. Now let me make amends and set down in brief the first acts of my reign:

1. The royal bodyguard has been doubled and a dozen gentlemen-at-arms of doubtful allegiance to the Crown (that is to say, myself) have been 'promoted' to more distant commands; a handsome donative has facilitated these measures.

2. I have removed Schmidt from his comfortable post as Quartermaster-General and have appointed him to the command of the household troops. He knows nothing of tactics

and less of strategy—so much the better; his loyalty is undoubted. My intuition—a useful term implying that there is no support in logic—tells me that he will not fail to disclose to me the faintest suspicion of disaffection within the ranks. This is the stuff of which quartermasters are made. You sign for your loyalty on the appropriate form and are required to hand it back intact at the end of the day. Quartermasters know there is a bad cheese in the store and do not have to count the rats to arrive at this conclusion.

3. Crappswein is under house arrest. This is a useful expedient that I have borrowed from [*illegible—Ed.*], quite as effective as the dungeon and less expensive to the State of Denmark. Grunwald is in process of drawing the indictment, not strictly speaking a task for the Chief Justice, but what of that if it carries the fiat of the Attorney-General? (Grunwald did not mind that aspect of it—he is a man of the world—but did not much relish my suggestion that I might look over a draft of it. He seems to forget I am a rusticated lawyer.) When the trial comes before him in due course he can scarcely be heard to complain (in my presence, at least) that there are any faults in the process. Perhaps for this reason I had better pass his draft without change?

For the time being the Commander-in-Chief is—incredibly— King Claudius. I have given it out that it would be improper to replace Crappswein until the charges against him are proved or disproved. Meanwhile it is also assiduously put about that the King is minded to carry the war into Norway as generalissimo. A likely story!

4. I have sent confidential dispatches to the old King of Norway. Entrusted with this mission are *two* ambassadors, Cornelius and Voltimand. (Did I mention that Voltimand is safe back in the fold?—at a price.) Cornelius is appointed as of right, being of the establishment and in the cant term a career diplomat, a misleading phrase which covertly implies that he is more concerned with his career than with the service of the State; this casts no shadow on him, a model of rectitude— merely holds up a mirror to the vile thraldom of the mob to tendentious slogans.

Voltimand I have translated to the diplomatic service from Polonius's intelligence corps, but his function remains the same:

to keep a watch on Cornelius. (Sigismund will of course continue to watch Voltimand.) Several heads (Polonius' included)
have wagged sadly over this decision. Why send a man who
has failed in one mission on another? Answer: because he will
exert himself all the more to avoid a second failure. Voltimand
was visibly affected by my confidence. In any case, failure is
acceptable, disloyalty not.

The purpose of these dispatches? First to assure the old King
that this daily cast of brazen cannon and foreign mart for
implements of war are no more than *defensive* measures; even
so, defensive against the aggressive designs (if any) of the
Prince Fortinbras. I have assured Norway of an enduring
peace (on terms) and have suggested certain positive measures
of disarmament, provided of course these are mutual. Need
I say also that I have deplored the evident risk that the war,
once begun, may escalate?

As for Voltimand, I have privately instructed him to add
certain riders concerning my nephew Hamlet, which are not
committed to the written dispatch.

7th July

An unpopular but necessary measure which I have adopted
on the recommendation of Sigismund—now chief of my secret
police, a change of nomenclature but not of function—concerns
the arrangements for the coronation (the wedding, too, it goes
without saying) in five days' time. Viewing the concourse from
the upper storeys of buildings and from balconies adjacent to
the route is interdicted.

It is given out that this is in the interests of the public safety—
a nice choice of phrase, so I think, for the safety of the public
now reposes largely in my person. Both in the interests of the
public and my own I am disinclined to submit myself—or
Gertrude, for that matter—to the danger and indignity of
missiles propelled from embrasures or half-bricks dropped
on the State coaches. But it has been advertised widely
that many of the houses and balconies alongside the route
will not support the weight of the spectators. An unfortunate
incident at the late King's funeral, when part of a balcony
subsided over a cat's-meat shop, has been a trifle enlarged by

F

Sigismund; in fact it just tilted over at a steep angle and decanted its incumbents on to the public highway with nothing worse than one broken arm and a few cuts and bruises. Still, as Sigismund remarks, the occupants of balconies cannot, like cats, count upon nine lives; it is unwise to tempt providence further. And as *I* have remarked to *him*, such incidents may be tolerated at obsequies, but not on such a festive and even unique occasion as a coronation and royal marriage combined.

Sigismund's admirable suggestion will have some few beneficial side effects. Thus, people will be forced into the streets, whether they like it or not, so we should have none of that raggety look of a blighted beanfield which is always so painful to the court on royal occasions—in brief a press, not a motley of garlic-breathing bystanders. True, this will make it more strenuous work for the soldiery to restrain and control the mob. But Sigismund rightly points out that a would-be assassin needs some freedom of movement; a man with both arms pinioned by the crowd and held back by two ranks of linked halberdiers is in no shape to experiment with ballistics, to make signals to confederates or to choose a momentary opening of the cordon to irrupt into the processional. There is some horse sense in this.

I had all but forgot to mention that on the pretext of enforcing this measure I have endorsed a royal warrant of search of all upper storeys of scheduled buildings. Sigismund's men will work in twos and threes, ostensibly on the look-out for miscreants and hidden weapons, though it may be doubted if they will discover any human life save the ailing and bed-rid who are exempt from the order. But I confidently expect an interesting report upon the activities of certain political factions (to name none)—so singularly lax are they in ridding themselves of incriminating evidence.

8th July

A fearful nightmare. I was crowned King of Denmark and married to Gertrude on the same day. The mob was hostile. The Archbishop mumbled the coronation rubrics. Twice the organ pealed insanely at the wrong moment and then whined into an embarrassing silence, with a tremor which could be felt in every corner of the vast cathedral. I sweated under my robes and the crown was too heavy and fitted badly, chafing my temples.

Then came the wedding. Gertrude's face was averted from me as she stood by my side at the altar, and when the Archbishop called for her response she replied in a shrill voice 'No!' And a great shout of 'Crucify him!' went up from the congregation, like a hallelujah, yet unlike. Then at last Gertrude turned to me, but now she was no longer Gertrude but Penelope, and in a voice of infinite sweetness and compassion she again said 'No!' Then all the people clamoured 'Crucify her!' and the organ thundered in unison. At this Gertrude, still changed to Penelope, whispered: 'I love you, Claudius. God knows I love you.'

I awoke with a splitting headache. Have arranged for another trial fitting of the crown.

12th July

J'ai vécu.[1]

14th July

I continue to record this journal in code. This is partly from habit, partly to preserve it from curious eyes—not uniformly those from which it was to be protected when I began it.

I feel a faint sense of shame in committing to paper, albeit in code, what lawyers discreetly call the secrets of the marriage chamber. And indeed I would not, but that I stand, as it were, incredulous of my own testimony and must give it the substance and form of a *procès-verbal*. How readily does one contract the habit of these empty forensic phrases! I mean, of course, the substance, but not the form.

Such were the fatigues of the wedding that even the Queen, accustomed as she is to the intolerable burdens of royalty, was utterly prostrate by nightfall. And by prostrate I do not mean supine. As for myself, nursed, it is true, in the tradition but with less campaigning experience than she, and taxed with the

---

[1] With this concise entry Claudius disposes of the ceremonial of the coronation and the wedding in its entirety. As to the mode of expression, see his comments at p. 8, *ante*, which seem apt in the context. Evidently if there is to be a charge of plagiarism it must be laid elsewhere.—*Ed.*

double toll of the coronation and the wedding, I should willingly have sold the State of Denmark to my nephew Hamlet
for two groats and the favour of a passport to England—a
tributary State possessed of a climate which, by repute, is even
viler than our own.

So much for that night when by common consent we slept
apart, she in the great double—I might with justice say
quadruple—bed of the royal bedchamber, in the company of
absurdly cavorting Cupids and a number of insipid and rotund
Venuses; I in the adjoining King's chamber, which is providentially furnished in a more austere taste.

But last night there was no escape from it.

I procrastinated, I must own, but eventually I presented
myself in the royal bedchamber, attired in my purple dressing-
gown with gold and cerise dragons embroidered on the cuffs
and collar—a neat design which seemed to me to put the Cupids
a little out of countenance.

I found Gertrude sitting up in bed at work on her embroidery.

'The light in here is appalling,' she said.

'I will get the Ministry of Works on to it,' I said.

'Oh do, Claudius,' said she, putting her stitching on one side.

She gave a great sigh and said: 'I like you in that dressing-
gown; it suits you so much better than those hideous coronation
robes. But all the same you look as though you had indigestion.'

I felt as though I had indigestion, as a matter of fact.

'Do I?' I said; I couldn't think of anything else.

'Are you frightened of me, Claudius?' she asked.

I fiddled with my dressing-gown cord. 'Well, not exactly,'
I replied. 'You see, I 've never been married before.'

'You have good reason to be apprehensive,' she said. 'I was
frightened to death when I married Hamlet. Most brides, I am
told, get over it. But you see I never did—it just went on
and on.'

'What went on and on?' I asked. People say this is the sort
of question that stamps me as a lawyer. I suppose it does, but
then I do like to know what people are talking about.

'Come and sit down,' she said, patting the bed and heaving
herself over a bit. I did as bid.

There was a pause, and after a while, as though choosing

her words, she said she surmised I feared that she would make excessive demands upon me of a certain character.

'Oh no, not at all,' I said.

As a matter of fact she had hit the nail on the head. But I confess I was curious to know whether Penelope was right in asserting that she was boiled shrimp all over. Possibly a compensation for the labour of love? But I recognized that it was not the right moment to indulge such fancies.

'Well now, I will tell you something, Claudius,' she was saying. 'I have a dreadful confession to make.'

When people talk like this I am always alarmed; there are so many possibilities. I even had time to wonder whether Gertrude could have had a hand in the murder of Hamlet, but I dismissed the thought as unworthy of me and out of character with her.

She did not seem to be in any haste to tell me what was weighing on her conscience. 'Come along,' she said, 'and get into bed, because my feet are frozen. I do hope you are going to be a *warm* husband? I need one.'

'Warm perhaps. Not hot, mind you,' I said. But I was beginning to feel chilly myself, so I got into bed with her. It was more friendly that way, and when I had warmed up a bit I took the dressing-gown off.

'Now,' she said, 'do you really think I am going to make excessive demands?'

The conversation seemed to be getting out of my control. Obviously I *did* think so. I thought of Gertrude putting away all those cream puffs and pastries; I don't know what this had to do with it except an inept association of different appetites. However, I dishonestly said 'No'. I said I had assumed her demands would be normal, not excessive; in any case I did not care for the word 'demands'.

This was an unfortunate word for me to pick upon as it happens.

'Well, I must tell you, Claudius, for you might just as well know now as later. Your brother bored me stiff with his demands.'

'Bored you stiff?' I said stupidly.

I obliterate the rest of her remarks, some of which may have been a trifle exaggerated. At least I shall obliterate all but one, which happened to catch my imagination, if not my credence. She swears that the only way she could obtain any rest from my brother was to munch an apple during sexual commerce.

'So I do hope', she said, 'that you will not expect too much of me.'

Not for the first time I did not know what to say to this either.

'Come along,' she said. 'You can warm up my feet.'

So we went to sleep. Gertrude's feet were like ice-blocks, but they warmed up after a time.

She is, by the way, pink all over. Not at all mottled.

CHAPTER EIGHT

25th July

The day after tomorrow there will be assembled the first
Council of State since my accession. There have been some
mutterings about adjournments; but there has been method in
my madness, for I have been awaiting the ambassadors to
Norway. Few except Polonius and Sigismund are aware of the
mission; both Voltimand and Cornelius are so often absent
from Elsinore on special missions that it is unlikely that their
absence together will have aroused curiosity.

The pair of them returned yesterday and I received them
immediately in audience. The old King's message is cordial and
conciliatory; so far as it goes it is satisfactory, but it does not
go far enough. It is evident he would welcome a non-aggression
pact (if I may coin a term), and we are at one on that. But his
assurances count for nothing so long as Fortinbras is at large
with (as Cornelius and Voltimand report) a rabble at his heels
which bids fair to become a revolutionary army.

Norway slides gently round this awkward feature and harps
again querulously upon the supposed treachery of my nephew

73

Hamlet. What a distorting mirror! To read the old man's letter one would suppose that Hamlet is tramping the length and breadth of Denmark with bands of half-trained soldiery, instead of—as is the case—venting his spleen on me by caustic remarks and untimely reminders of his father's death. I confess that I have little patience with his exhibitionism. This now shows itself in inky cloaks and customary suits of solemn black— trappings and suits of woe made even more insupportable by his windy suspirations of forced breath. The emphasis, un-questionably, is on the 'forced'.

However, I have been led away from the subject. Norway, again. What is the sense of treating with a dotard who cannot command the dues of sovereignty? To borrow a legal phrase, we must have further and better particulars. I commended Cornelius and Voltimand on the partial success of their mission and on their good sense in referring back for further orders. They are to report to the Council—in which matter I have not failed to rehearse them—and immediately thereafter they are to return to Norway with new dispatches.

These dispatches I am in course of drafting, for I am my own foreign secretary. They are brief and to the point. Norway shall stand surety for his nephew Fortinbras, I for my nephew Hamlet. Allowing that Fortinbras may have ten thousand men at arms and an unnumbered mob at his bidding, Hamlet none —nothing, in short, but his popularity and posing, only an imbecile could suppose that I have the best of this bargain.

26th July

It has greatly vexed me to decide whether or not to admit the Queen to Council meetings. She has little aptitude and no inclination for matters of State. When—as sometimes happens— she brings her native common sense to bear upon a seemingly intricate question, she goes about it with as much delicacy and tact as a tree falling upon a house. My late brother solved the problem in his own casual way, giving her liberty to attend or absent herself as she pleased. In consequence she seldom attended. Now that I know her better—a great deal better— I realise that she must have presented herself at my brother's last strange convention of councillors (admittedly not a plenary session) for the express purpose of taxing him with the un-resolved question of the regency.

It is not without a wry recognition of my brother's qualities that I find myself adopting the same or like measures. I have determined that Gertrude should at least attend the first Council meeting of my reign; we must present a consolidated front. Apart from this, I need her help in the much more acute problem of finding suitable and harmless employment for the Prince Hamlet.

Hamlet is indeed a thorn in the side. Gertrude and I have had long and inconclusive discussions about him. I find her more percipient than I could have hoped, so in the main we are agreed upon our conclusions, even if we reason differently. For example, according to Gertrude, such failings as may be discerned in her son may one and all be tracked to that hot-bed of vice and so-called liberal thought, the University of Witten-berg. Now, as all Denmark knows, I am no fanatic for the University of Wittenberg. But many have passed through Wittenberg scatheless and not a few to their own advantage. A youth makes of Wittenberg what he may. It is like a hot-house which brings out the best or the worst in young plants; nor do I modify an earlier statement of mine that it is a hot-house of balderdash and twittery. Gertrude may choose to liken it to a dung-heap, but the metaphor counts for naught: only the bad seed will fail.

At all events we were agreed that Hamlet should be dis-couraged from returning to Wittenberg. Speaking for myself, I care not how malign its influence may be. I plan to have my nephew under constant surveillance, with just so much opportunity to attempt further and treasonable corre-spondence with Fortinbras as will support an indictment. Wittenberg offers him too much scope. Did I mention that Sigismund's painstaking search, conducted on coronation day, threw up some evidence on this subject of a highly incriminating character? Unfortunately there are points yet to be substantiated.

27th July

First Council meeting. Traditionally in each new session an occasion for the King's Speech, which resembles a small sausage meat of policy wrapped in a thick pastry of platitude. My brother was content to leave the composition of the King's Speech to his first minister and from the steps of the throne would then mouth with evident distaste the graceful periods and flower of Polonius's craft, mangling the syntax and stressing the wrong points—an evergreen piece of buffoonery.

But if my brother chastised the councillors with whips, I shall, for my part, and pursuant to precedent, chastise them with scorpions. The King's Speech was of my own composition, and upon it I had lavished an infinity of care. I flatter myself that the meat and pastry were combined in unexceptionable proportions.

After much deliberation I resolved that Hamlet should attend. His situation resembles my own when his father reigned—that is, he attends by royal command or not at all. To exclude him might be construed amongst his adherents—and some others—as a graceless mark of disfavour. To invite him must count to my credit and yet be all the more odious to him. Moreover there are more practical considerations. I had so spiced the sausage meat, most liberally in the matter of Fortinbras, as to make it little to his taste. And then there was the question of his return to Wittenberg, in regard to which the Queen had promised to exert her influence.

I think I shall set down in brief the substance of my speech, which was well received by all except Hamlet. True, it is recorded in the official minutes, and at greater length, but despite all precautions I have no confidence that the minutes will survive undoctored. Too many official histories are reflections of forgery.

On second thoughts it would be too tedious to set it out *in extenso*. Instead I shall set down my *memoria technica*, interspersed with a few comments (special phrases noted in italics; these archaisms are caviare to the general):

1. My brother Hamlet

Memory green. Befitting to bear hearts in grief. Whole kingdom likewise. *Contracted in one brow of woe*. But must be practical. Look to safety of State of Denmark. Combine wisdom with sorrow (*wisest* sorrow). Think on him with remembrance of ourselves.

2. Gertrude

Sometime sister, now our Queen. Introduce sentiment. *Imperial jointress to this war-like State.* Stress 'war-like'; we are not out of the wood. For weaker brethren amplify meaning of 'jointress'; remember some unfamiliar with legal terms. Next point: they are all committed to our policy and in fact authors of it: *Nor have we herein barred your better wisdoms, which have freely gone with this affair along: for all, our thanks.* Stress 'better' wisdoms. Remember the other Claudius, forced into the imperial purple. Perhaps repeat 'better', after the manner of Crappswein? But must not overdo it.

Note: Modest smiles at G., genial looks for H.
    Appear to address his dissidents at point 'for *all,* our thanks'.

3. Fortinbras

Frequent looks at H. Pour scorn on Fortinbras. Reminder of lands lost by his father to our *most valiant brother.* F. now importuning surrender of same. Contemptuous note: *Holding a weak supposal of our worth, or thinking by our late dear brother's death our state to be disjoint and out of frame.*

Note: Gaze steadfastly at H.
Conclude: '*So much for him*'; relieve tension here.
Memo: Remind Polonius to prompt claque for laugh.

4. Dispatches to Norway

Summon Cornelius and Voltimand. Take their report as read. Outline purpose of their new mission. Stress '*levies, lists and proportions*', all made up by Fortinbras out of Norway's subject. *Norway to suppress his further gait herein.* Make it clear that ambassadors are not given plenary powers, no more than the *scope of delated articles allow.*

Memo: Ensure their departure before the Council ask that these delated articles are laid before them.

5. Laertes

He to petition for return to France. (In fact I do not care to have him here making further trouble with Hamlet.) Polonius to join in the charade. Concede permission as a favour to Polonius.

> *Comment:* A calculated risk, accepted on the advice of Polonius. Our insistence that Hamlet remains will be all the more galling for the Prince. He shall see who is the master now.

6. Hamlet

Fully rehearsed with Gertrude. Be all geniality. Praise his filial piety, with reservations: *'Tis sweet and commendable in your nature, Hamlet, to give these mourning duties to your father.* Yet some barbs too: *You are the most immediate to our throne.* (How will he like that?) Conclude harshly: *For your intent in going back to school in Wittenberg, it is most retrograde to our desire.*

Well, as I said of Fortinbras, so much for him. The King's Speech passed off well. I felt myself in command of the situation. Gertrude was a tower of strength and contrived, almost, to wheedle Hamlet out of his black mood. I concluded the session on a quiet note. 'This gentle and unforced accord of Hamlet sits smiling to my heart.' Unforced? I wonder.

29th July

Gertrude confides to me that little Ophelia has been to her in great distress. It seems she has been successively lectured by her brother, Laertes, and her father, Polonius.

It is a little difficult to piece the story together at second hand. In any case, what reliance can be placed upon hearsay (feminine) evidence? For what it is worth, I gather that the wooden Laertes improved the shining hour of his departure for France by warning his sister to preserve her virtue intact against the importunities of Hamlet. I have no particular reason to believe that the life which Laertes leads in Paris is that of a Stylites, but I must make allowance for the two favourite pastimes of the human race: offering unwelcome advice and declining it.

Laertes evidently surpassed himself with some quaint saws of such a lyrical pattern that I can only suppose that he borrowed them from his father. Thus Ophelia is to keep 'in the rear of her affection' (which for some obscure reason has convulsed the literal Gertrude); and—what puzzles me more—it seems she is to adopt some new fetish of narcissism and henceforth undress herself in the moonlight.

It pleased me to learn, after so much rubbish, that Ophelia gave a good account of herself and quoted the old 'primrose path' back at her brother. She is not lacking in spirit. The only question is whether he will have the wit to take the point that she recognizes his parade of concern for her virtue as a mere cover for his political manœuvres against Hamlet.

Be this as it may, Polonius, it seems, played the heavy father in the most ponderous manner imaginable. Hence little Ophelia's tears. She adores her father, her brother and Hamlet. First one, then another, abuses her. *Per* Polonius: she is to be somewhat scanter of her maiden presence; she speaks like a green girl, etc. Polonius compares Hamlet's vows to 'sanctified and pious bonds': so says G.; obviously it should be 'bawds', but dear Ophelia would scarce know the word.

III

The Antic Disposition

CHAPTER NINE

30th July

Fantastic rumours circulate about an apparition of the late
King, which is said to manifest itself, soon after the stroke of
midnight, on the battlements of Elsinore.

At first I was of a mind to dismiss them out of hand. But
then I remembered that strange experience of mine in the
Council chamber, the conviction that I was in the ghostly
presence of my brother, seated at the head of the table;
rationally I attribute it to sleeplessness and overstrain. Yet
what is reason but the fallible operation of an overrated and
inadequate instrument, the human brain? Reason is what tells
you to fish the moon's reflection out of the duckpond with a
drag-net.

There remains a sense of unease. Could it be that for a few
moments, before passing into that dead faint, I stood upon the
threshold of the unknown, the frontier between the material
and the spiritual?

Sceptic as I am, I am selective in my scepticism. I believe
in the sea-serpent. And why not? So many sailors have seen it;

I cannot believe they are all liars, for they gain nothing by lying. And if it were a fit issue to be brought to trial, I should regard it as abundantly proved on the testimony of unexceptionable witnesses that spirits walk the earth—ay, and under the earth. I recall from my early days of idle and pleasurable study in the palace library—now I do nothing but study minutes and reports—many well-attested narratives, in much circumstantial detail, of spirits above and below. Indeed it is said that labourers in the mines commonly encounter subterranean spirits attired like themselves. Some of them busy themselves about the work, winning, carrying and storing the ore and applying themselves to like labours; yet it seems that even in the depths of the earth there must be good spirits and evil, for some thus put themselves to the tasks and others (for whom, one must suppose, there are purgatories yet in reserve) set themselves to affrighting the pioneers with blood-curdling shrieks and monstrous rumblings.[1]

Though reluctant to give shape and substance to idle talk, I decided to call for a confidential report from Sigismund; then, after reflection, I thought it might make less stir if I referred it to Schmidt, for it is clearly a matter within his command of the household troops. What decided me in the end to make further inquiry was the intelligence that Horatio—bosom friend to Hamlet, and would God their natures or stations in life might be exchanged!—had insinuated himself into the night watch and done duty with one of the regular sentries, by name Marcellus. And it seems it is Horatio who has given substance

---

[1] It is hardly to be supposed that Claudius had access to Lavater's *Of Ghostes and Spirites walking by Nyght* (1572), for obvious reasons of chronology, but it may well be that he derived his information from a common source. There are remarkable resemblances with the following passage cited from Lavater by Professor Dover Wilson (*What Happens in Hamlet*):

Pioners or diggers for mettal, do affirme, that in many mines, there appeare straunge shapes and spirites, who are apparelled like unto other labourers in the pit. These wander up and down in caves and underminings, & seeme to besturre them selves in all kinde of labour, as to digge after the veine, to carry together the oare, to put it into baskets and to turne the winding whele to drawe it up, when in very deede they do nothing lesse.

Be not dismayde, though thou heare some spirit stir and make a noyse, for in case hee rumble onely to make thee afrayde, care not for him, but lette hym rumble so long as he wyll, for if he see thee without feare, hee wyll soone depart from thee.

The concluding text would be more reassuring if Lavater had stated in plain terms the fate of the craven miner whose fears were *not* adequately concealed.—*Ed.*

to these stories of the apparition. Though Horatio is a fellow
student with Hamlet, I know him too well to suppose that he
is deranged by the pestilential vapours of Wittenberg. It is my
belief that his scepticism is at least the equal of mine.[1] Thus I
should not care to dismiss his opinion lightly. By all accounts
Horatio is quite persuaded that he himself saw the phantom—
whatever it may be, a spirit of health or goblin damned (to
employ a trite phrase): this is enough, in my judgment, to
establish a *prima facie* case.

As for the testimony of Marcellus, Bernardo, Francesco and
the rest, I should not rate it at a pin's fee, so credulous are the
soldiery and prone to prey on their own and each other's fears.
It is an ancient jape, doubtless practised under the Roman
centurions, to seat recruits upon a hillside at dusk, announcing
that an enemy patrol is to creep upon them unawares. The first
man to notice suspect movements of the enemy patrol is to
stand up and describe what he sees. This deception never fails.
The recruits strain their eyes and imaginations in the unaccustomed shades and soon one springs to his feet—then another
and another. The competition to identify the enemy waxes
and the circumstantial detail grows apace. Of course, there
never was an enemy patrol. Dancing shapes and patterns in
the moonlight or quivering bushes in the evening breeze supply
all that is needed for those unused to the tormenting doubts
of the night sentinel. Even so, with the lesson learnt, young
soldiers as yet unhardened by campaign will take sheep's eyes
reflected by the moon for the glint of brass, buckle or spear
of the foe. Too often has my hard-earned slumber been shat-
tered for no better result than tough mutton in the quartermaster's store.

31st July

A serious talk with Schmidt, who has the eye of a quartermaster
for detail and has already acquainted himself with the parentage, background, character and capabilities of his small and
specialized command, to say nothing of their weaknesses, which
is more to the point. He tells me that Francesco has not—at
least by his account—seen the phantom; none of the night

[1] Which by some standards may not put it very high.—*Ed.*

watch have seen it save Bernardo and Marcellus. Perhaps I should modify my earlier scepticism as respects the evidence of Bernardo, who is, says Schmidt, a stolid soldier: a little stupid, but all solid worth and thus of little use to us. Marcellus is a poet *manqué*, vain, changeable, unreliable, corruptible, yet well enough liked in the barrack-room to pass under the name of Cocky Bob.[1]

I determined that we should try the easier gamble and make a bid for Marcellus, even if we have to discount his narrative. Schmidt is to offer such inducements as occasion may prompt. These may fittingly include a *douceur* of some sort; I have left it to him to devise ways and means, but have warned him against such crude devices as bribery, which might corrupt the whole national guard. Besides, what is the point of that, when an appeal to the man's oath of allegiance and a vague offer of promotion would be equally effective and a great deal cheaper? Schmidt is to do what he can; and of course I was at pains to display incredulity, offering as explanation that I was concerned to put an end to these absurdities for the preservation of morale.

I have good reason to believe that Horatio has already disclosed to Hamlet what he has seen and is even now planning to bring him into rapport with his father's spirit. I can only suppose that both of them must be endowed with the Nemean lion's nerve. At all events I told Schmidt that Hamlet and Horatio are at liberty to take the night air when and as they please, so long as they do not interfere with the security of the palace. I did *not* tell him that I have ordered Sigismund, by way of double check (or treble, if you count the ghost) to detail two of his most capable men to watch the proceedings; one of these is to follow Hamlet and the other Marcellus. Nor are they to be told the watchword; Sigismund's spies must keep aloof and look after their own safety. It would never do for our secret service and soldiery to work in concert; this could so easily lead to collaboration!

2nd August

Marcellus has spoken freely to Schmidt and required little persuasion to do so. It seems that he and Bernardo have seen

[1] *Robertus erectus*; untranslatable and somewhat softened in the rendering.
—*Ed.*

the shape on two occasions during the night watch. It appears about the hour of midnight, stalks across the platform, then vanishes for a while and again reappears. It is the spectre of a tall man in full armour, with visor up. Marcellus declares it was in the image of the late King himself and in his own armour; he recognized the King's beard (following his poetic bent, he describes it as 'a sable silvered'!). I was diverted by some circumstantial detail, presumably added for verisimilitude: for example, he noticed two dents in the armour, about the middle of the breastplate, which can be very readily checked against the original, though what this may prove is beyond Schmidt's comprehension and my own.

According to Marcellus the apparition makes anguished motions as though to speak, but there is no utterance.

Of this idle talk I can make nothing. But at least Schmidt has impressed upon Marcellus that his oath of allegiance transcends all other oaths of whatsoever kind, no matter by whom or on what sacred relics sworn.

3rd August

I hear that Hamlet has been grumbling about the impress of shipwrights and the cost of armaments in general. Like his father before him he supposes that warfare is no more than a parade-ground evolution conducted on foreign soil, with some attendant risk; logistics and supplies count for nothing. It is diverting to note various theories now in circulation, which he adopts by turns or in combination, however incongruous. First, the State of Denmark is in course of being ruined by the expense of the arms programme. Secondly, the King seeks aggrandizement at the expense of his subjects, having no genuine intention of using these arms against another nation. Yet he hopes to curry favour with them by appearing to support the aggressive policies of his predecessor, though in fact deceiving them in this as in all else. Thirdly, he is not spending the money on armaments at all but upon trifles and extravagances about the court—palace banquets and such. And so on.

I gather that my recent decision to engage a personal bodyguard of Switzers has not been well received. This is at least a logical complaint: it makes my assassination more difficult to contrive.

4th August

The business of the ghost unfolds, as it were, backwards. Now I have a full confidential report on a visit to the platform by Hamlet and Horatio at dusk today, doubtless contrived by Horatio to coincide with the evening watch of that stalwart pair, Bernardo and Marcellus. In conformity with normal practice of the guard they do 'two hours on and four hours off'; this must have been the first watch, from which they would be relieved at 7.30 p.m. in time to take post again at 11.30 p.m. I must possess my soul in patience for the report of tonight's visitation—the more so as Hamlet and Horatio have arranged to be present, and Sigismund's men have been alerted.

Evidently to disarm suspicion that this evening's meeting was contrived, Hamlet was at pains to make it appear that it was his first encounter with Horatio since he last saw him at Wittenberg. 'What, in faith make you from Wittenberg? What is your affair in Elsinore?'—and so on. It seems also that Hamlet gave free rein to his mordant wit (if one may confuse equestrian terms), remarking in his acid way upon the brief interval between his father's death and his mother's remarriage. I suppose it would not help at all to remind him of the Mosaic duty of a brother towards the bereaved spouse? Indeed, if I remember rightly, a deceased husband's brother who shrank from the duty was an outcast in the eyes of Jah.

Be this as it may, Hamlet's comments on funeral baked meats which coldly furnished forth the marriage table do more justice to the sardonic whimsies of Wittenberg students than to the sumptuous fare provided for the wedding guests, largely at the charge of my own privy purse! But in common with most other young people, he judges everyone by his own standards and appetites, evidently supposing that bed is the be all and end all of matrimony. Of the political implications he is largely ignorant, save in his resentment of his own failure to seat himself on his father's throne.

The report reveals that Hamlet showed better sense in his questioning of Horatio and the two sentries. Characteristically he tried to trap the soldiery by the old method of a cross-examiner inviting a witness to overstate his evidence. Was the ghost fully armed? Yes, from top to toe. Therefore our friends M. and B. could not have recognized him! Horatio extricated them from this dilemma by explaining that the ghost wore his beaver up. (How do ghosts arrange this? It is hard to say.)

Then he tried the 'cheese-paring' method. How long was the spectre visible? According to Horatio, 'while one with moderate haste might tell a hundred'. But M. and B. both declared it was longer. After all, they have now seen it three times—twice on their own and once in company with Horatio. No wonder the visitations seem prolonged!

I must not fail to mention two diverting features of this report. It seems that Horatio used the selfsame phrase 'a sable silvered' in describing the late King's beard to Hamlet. Did he borrow it from Marcellus, or vice versa? Some of these reports make fascinating reading. Secondly, Horatio makes out that he knew the late King well ('these hands are not more like'); but this is absurd, for only five minutes before he was telling Hamlet that he had seen the King but *once*!

Unhappily these inconsistencies are no more than what one inevitably finds in any *procès-verbal*; they suggest to my mind that the substance of the narrative is more congruous with truth than falsehood. Only suborned or conniving witnesses agree amongst themselves in matters of detail.

5th August

I might have spared myself such curiosity to learn the tenor of last night's vigil, for it turns out to have been little more than a fiasco. Horatio and Hamlet presented themselves on the platform a little before midnight, where they engaged for a while in tendentious conversation with Marcellus. There is no mention in the report of Bernardo but, the night being exceptionally cold for August, I assume he was warming himself on a quick tour of the battlements. I must remember to inquire about this, for it is elementary that the sentries should work in pairs, the one covering the other.

The night was not propitious for the vigil, for a sharp drop in temperature had brought the sea vapours swirling up and around the ramparts. Thus, though Sigismund's spies found it easier to conceal themselves, they could see little of the others and had to rely more on their ears than their eyes. Allowing that they had so much difficulty in keeping track of those still in the flesh, perhaps it is no matter for wonder that they saw no ghost. But then neither of them—advisedly—had been warned to look out for it.

I must not censure the ghost for this. Quite the contrary. It seems to have made itself manifest to the others with its usual punctuality. So much is plain from the verbatim account of the proceedings—doubtless extremely puzzling to Sigismund's *voyeurs*, or should I say auditors.

So far as I can make any sense of the reports, after puzzling over them for a long while, I have evolved a theory. It is that the ghost works on various levels of communication. It may reveal itself not at all (as in the case of Sigismund's squad) or visually only (Hamlet now being the fourth to see it, unless I count myself in on this) or—query—audibly also, and on this level, I suspect, to Hamlet only. The last proposition is empirical, but then what is one to make of a series of comments and interjections, as faithfully reported by a trained man in the secret service, with pauses of varying length between, and nobody else present? Thus:

Hamlet: Whither wilt thou lead me? Speak; I'll go no further.
        (Short pause.)

Hamlet: I will.
        (Longer pause.)

Hamlet: Alas! poor ghost.
        (Short pause.)

Hamlet: Speak, I am bound to hear.

Hamlet: What?
        (Long interval here.)

Hamlet: O God!
        (Short pause.)

Hamlet: Murder!
        (Longer pause.)

Hamlet: Haste me to know 't, that I, with wings as swift as
    meditation or the thoughts of love
        (how characteristic of his style!)
  may sweep to my revenge.
        (Another, much longer pause.)

Hamlet: O my prophetic soul! My uncle!

What, I wonder, does he mean by *that*?

It seems that after a while Hamlet forgathered again with the others (Bernardo still *in absentia*—I really must look into this) and there was much horse-play as he demanded mock-solemn oaths of secrecy concerning the ghost, the last sworn on his sword. What is one to make of it? Hamlet is reported to have said it was an honest ghost. This much I believe, for I gather it conformed to type in subterranean movements while this charade was in progress. A most interesting phenomenon.

CHAPTER TEN

10th August

Were I Hamlet—perish the thought—I should hope so to comport myself as is befitting for a prince nearest to the throne of Denmark. But Hamlet's conduct becomes increasingly irresponsible and extravagant. Indeed one might suppose that he is determined to ratify the wisdom of our councillors and of the electoral college in the matter of the succession.

Now Polonius comes to me with a tale of rare absurdity, related to him by his daughter Ophelia. It seems that whilst Ophelia was sewing in her closet—she is a good girl and assiduous in her household motions—Hamlet burst in upon her like a storm trooper and was near to frightening her out of her wits. From what I can make of it Ophelia could not extract one word from him. He grabbed her by the wrist, then by the arm, studying her face the while; then pumped her arm up and down and nodded his head like an imbecile. Finally he let out a sigh fit to burst himself—a gargantuan draught such as may be encountered in the palace corridors.

These ham-handed histrionics by an indifferent performer,

duplicated by Polonius, who is another, were inexpressibly comical; I confess it was an effort to remain impassive.

Polonius described Hamlet's attire in detail: doublet unbraced, stockings fouled, ungartered and down-gyved to the ankle. Also the Prince was hatless, but of this I can make no sense, for why should he wear a hat in Ophelia's boudoir?

I was irresistibly reminded of a girl witness of my student days, complainant on a bastardy summons, under cross-examination concerning the colour of the putative father's hair. She replied indignantly that he had never removed his hat. By the time I had suppressed the recollection it was too late to ask why the Prince should appear covered in Ophelia's closet.

Be all this as it may, it is dreadful to contemplate my late dear brother's anger, were he not now occluded from his son's antics. He was a great stickler for correct deportment and attire; his clothes were worn as uniform, and he demanded of others a conformity in this as in all else. I shall not readily forget the occasion when a halberdier was deprived of seven days' leave for failing to polish his cap badge *on the inside*! Admittedly I do not carry my objections to informality to quite such a length. Indeed now that young men have taken to wearing their hair long, and may hardly be distinguished from the female of their species save by the narrowness of their hips and down on the chin—though either may be misleading—I have even been reproached for remarking that they are as much the slaves of fashion as we who follow the modes of maturity. But I draw the line at dirt and disarray. It is not seemly that Hamlet should present himself in our chief minister's house—or anywhere else for that matter—in such a squalid condition. I judge that he must have looked for all the world like the twin of my disreputable second cousin, the Margrave of Baeternick.

I shall have to talk with Gertrude about this.

Polonius seems to think that Hamlet is tormented by his passion for Ophelia. I doubt it. He would also have me believe that the distemper has been precipitated—or at least inflamed—by Ophelia's withdrawal of late of her 'maiden presence', pursuant to her father's homily some short while ago. To my thinking this is great nonsense. I deplore Hamlet's behaviour and poor Ophelia's distress. Yet more distressing and of more immediate moment is this evident dimming of the old man's perception and sense of proportion: he must ever take the centre of the stage, and thus it is that he prefers to reproach himself for a supposed error of judgment rather than stand limply in the wings.[1]

12th August

Theories multiply about the nature and cause of Hamlet's distemper. Polonius still adheres to his preposterous notion that Hamlet is going out of his mind for love of Ophelia. Gertrude says that he has had these moods before and accounts it no more than a passing disorder, a temporary condition of shock caused by his father's sudden death and what she is pleased to describe, with that bluntness of truth sometimes termed 'candour' (but vexatious, however described), as our o'erhasty marriage. This is all very fine, but if the marriage had not been 'o'erhasty', I should like to know what sort of a pickle we should all be in now.

Penelope, whose opinion I have also solicited, offers me an even less palatable explanation, saying that rumours now circulate about the court of further revelations by the ghost, which, like the sons of Levi, is surely taking too much upon it. If these are to be credited, Hamlet told Horatio that the ghost told *him* that I murdered the King to secure the crown and supplant him in the Queen's bed.

It is impossible at second or third hand to sift this hearsay, but it seems that the ghost described me in such unflattering terms as an incestuous and adulterate beast and remarked that my natural gifts were poor in comparison with his—or, as I should say for avoidance of misunderstanding, with those of the late King, for it is unreasonable to expect me to compete with this talented spectre. On the other hand there was no consistency in the references to Gertrude, who was described at one point as a 'radiant angel' and at another as 'a most pernicious woman'. Obviously she cannot be both, and in my opinion is neither. Penelope suggests, with some ingenuity, that the former is the ghost's version and the latter Hamlet's. If

[1] Translator's licence, the stage at that time being circular.—*Ed.*

this is so, it seems that Hamlet is now minded to make himself as disagreeable to his mother as he is towards myself.

I have told Gertrude as much of this as I deem fit for her ears; it is pointless and would be unkind to add to her concern. Happily she is convinced that there is nothing seriously amiss with Hamlet. She has conceived the notion that he merely needs to be shaken out of his present mood by innocent social diversion, preferably in the company of young men of his own age. She has suggested that those nitwits Rosencrantz and Guildenstern should be deputed (in her phrase) to 'take him out of himself'—as though he were zero to be subtracted from zero. Though I believe this comparison to be apt, it is more suited to Penelope's intellect and I refrained from mentioning it to Gertrude.

In my view the diagnosis is wrong, so the treatment will not effect a cure. However, to humour the Queen, I consented to the proposal, only stipulating that the two playboys report to us anything they may glean concerning the true cause of the Prince's affliction. Thus has it been ordered, the Queen making a pretty enough speech to the pair, albeit expressed more as entreaty than as command, which was not as I should have wished, and offered Rosencrantz the opportunity of an impudent comment which I allowed to pass. I judge that Hamlet's wits are in better shape than many others about this court, so much misdoubt the carriage of this affair.

17th August

Polonius having sought another audience to discuss what he is pleased to term Hamlet's lunacy, I asked Gertrude to attend the consultation. I confess I am weary of the subject. Allowing that the Prince is my cross, he is also the Queen's son.

We were no sooner started on this topic than unexpectedly the ambassadors from Norway were announced—three weeks to the day since they embarked on their mission. Impatient to hear them, I postponed the tedious business of Hamlet's aberrations.

Voltimand's report amounts to this. The old King pretends that he had supposed that his nephew's levies were a preparation against the Polack, though how in God's name he could

tolerate the levying of arms within his realm against the
Polack, or to any other end, passes my comprehension. But
'better looked into'—he says, at the instance of our ambassadors—he admits that it was a preparation against ourselves.

It seems that Norway has rebuked Fortinbras and we are
asked to believe that Fortinbras has submitted himself to the
rebuke and forsworn assay of arms against us. A likely story!
The old zany has accepted his nephew's show of submission
with transports of joy, has settled three thousand crowns on
him—and that not for life, but in fee!—and has granted him a
lawful commission to employ the enlisted soldiery against the
Polack. In brief, the crime is not merely condoned, it is
rewarded. To cap it all, Voltimand handed me a paper seeking
safe passage for this mountebank's levies through our realm.

My hand was shaking so much with suppressed indignation
that it was with difficulty that I could hold the paper, but I
contrived somehow to thank Voltimand and Cornelius for their
labours and even bade them dine tonight. They are not to
blame for this fiasco. I said I should take time for consideration,
passing it off so. This is what comes of treating with a dotard!

18th August

I see that, in my vexation over the failure of the mission to
Norway, I forgot to record in my journal the follies which
succeeded when Cornelius and Voltimand had withdrawn.
Polonius was at his most prolix, much to Gertrude's dudgeon.
Latterly, in the privacy of our apartments, she has variously
described him as a dunderpate, a windbag and an obsequious
clown, and in more exuberant moments has applied even more
opprobrious epithets, fit only for the stews of Naples. When
she flags for inspiration, she contents herself with observing (in
a cant phrase) that he suffers from verbal incontinence.

Had Gertrude not married a king—well, in truth two kings—
she would have made a superlative barmaid, she is so much
down to earth. Polonius's natural element, on the other hand,
is air. I see small children in little back gardens flying balloons
gaily coloured in red, blue and yellow. They remind me of
my chief minister. I serve as the cord that tethers him to
terra firma.

I suspect that Polonius has irked Gertrude for many a long year, but it is only now that by chance she can agreeably mix grievance with prejudice in those nice proportions so much to the relish of mankind and her sex in especial. The focus of her complaint is the interference of Polonius in the affair of Ophelia and Hamlet, though whether in truth she complains more of the insult to the Prince implicit in the instruction that Ophelia should withdraw her maiden favours or of the consequent hardship to Ophelia is hard to judge. But grievances, like weeds, will grow in any soil and it is idle to inquire.

To make matters worse, the dear old man, sensing my annoyance over Voltimand's report, addressed himself to the Queen, first in the ludicrous manner that he affects as a lady-killer and then—stumbling over himself—bluntly stated that her son was mad. Though the Queen is blessed with an equable temperament, this exceeded all limits of human endurance; as he seemed about to deliver himself of a lecture on the nature of madness in general, she cut him short, saying with asperity 'more matter with less art'. I admired her for that. Barmaid or queen, she is an admirable woman, nor am I sorry that in the grip of circumstance I espoused her.

To come to the point—as eventually Polonius did—we were shown a letter said to have been written by Hamlet to Ophelia. This Polonius read with many justified strictures on the style, taking exception in particular to the word 'beautified', though to my thinking there would be few students left in Wittenberg if literary aptitude became the criterion for sanity. There was an obscure reference to Ophelia's white bosom (in decency as a father he might have spared the Queen this), followed by four lines of doggerel, which my fatal memory has retained:

Doubt that the stars are fire;
  Doubt that the sun doth move;
Doubt truth to be a liar;
  But never doubt I love.

I cannot myself detect any trace of madness in this con-coction. The first two lines are evidently framed as self-evident propositions, such as would be accepted without demur by any middle-aged burgher puffing his clay pipe. But what do we know of the stars? Are they fire or brimstone or molten lava or (as I have heard it suggested, though I cannot credit it) just swirling, overheated gases? And why assume that the sun moves? Who knows but that the sun may be stationary and that it is the rotation of the earth which creates an optical illusion of the sun crossing the heavens? As for truth being a liar, as Pontius Pilate rightly asked (but the question remains unanswered): What is truth?

The letter continued in prose (if it may be so termed) and concluded, as I clearly remember, with the phrase 'Thine evermore, most dear lady, whilst this machine is to him, Hamlet'. I ask myself, is this what a demented person writes? Certainly not. The demented as a rule assume a false premiss— say that the writer has just laid an egg or that he has discovered the elixir of life—and the argument then proceeds with un-exceptionable logic to a faultless conclusion. You do not find him in comparison with a machine unless there is some good reason for it. No—this is a botched job by an amateur.

'Came this from Hamlet to her?' said the Queen before Polonius had reached the end. This may have been her native common sense, but I flatter myself that a critical mind already burgeons in her so soon after our espousal.

I ventured to ask how Ophelia had received Hamlet's love. In truth I should like to see little Ophelia receive her deserts: an agreeable young man of good station and an affectionate disposition who would not submit her to needless stresses and strains (given a good heart I should not care if he were a little stupid). That was uppermost in my mind, though I also thought to test Polonius's notion that his daughter's rebuffs have unseated Hamlet's reason.

I had done better to leave the colloquy to him and Gertrude, for the old man, already piqued by Gertrude's stiffness, at once took umbrage and became absurdly heated, asking whether he had ever expressed a positive opinion and then been proved in the wrong. I could have mentioned several instances, but I shall choose my own moment for referring to them, if occasion requires. I replied curtly: 'Not that I know.' But so incensed was he that he asked to be decapitated if he proves wrong in his diagnosis of Hamlet's condition.

Thinking to stifle the discussion I asked for proof. Now it seems he has conceived the idea of spying on Hamlet and

Ophelia together. I mislike it, but if it does not prove that Hamlet is mad, it may prove that Polonius is. A minute or two after advising me to sever his head from his shoulders he was talking of retirement to tend his farm and carters. It is fatiguing to keep pace with his volatile fancies.

CHAPTER ELEVEN

20th August

More absurdities. Polonius has submitted a verbatim report of a conversation with Hamlet, which it seems took place within a few minutes of the consultation two days ago. This is adduced as further evidence of Hamlet's alleged madness, though to my mind it proves nothing except his ill manners and effrontery.

Polonius reports that no sooner had the Queen and I withdrawn with our attendants than Hamlet appeared in the doorway reading—or purporting to read—a book. In passing I may remark that people who read books whilst walking or eating in my opinion deserve to break their necks or die of abdominal ulcers; you cannot effectively carry on these activities in parallel—it is an affront to nature. However, I have no cause for concern in Hamlet's behalf, for as like as not the book is not for reading but for noting conversations overheard about the court.

I could wish I had been present at this encounter, for it seems that Hamlet was at his sharpest—or maddest, as one may choose. But sane or insane, it is deplorable that his nature should prompt or permit him to mock at this old man who has served the State so well and is surely deserving of compassion as his powers begin to fail him. It is all of a piece with my suspicions concerning Hamlet's harsh treatment of Ophelia. And Gertrude tells me that she has been subjected to the like. I much fear that there is an ugly streak in Hamlet, something which fastens on those weaker than himself.

Be this as it may, is it courteous to remark in the hearing of a greybeard that old men have grey beards? That their faces are wrinkled, their eyes purging thick amber and plum-tree gum? That they have a plentiful lack of wit, together with most weak hams? I think not. Nor does it count in mitigation, but rather to exacerbate the offence, that Hamlet—having doubtless rehearsed all this—should palm it off as the lucubrations of a third party, viz. the author of the book. Not content with this, he remarked that he shared the sentiments but held it not honesty to have it thus set down. Hamlet's subtlety is such that he bids fair to strangle himself with it. Could he have revealed more plainly that he is conscious of his own lack of breeding?

It seems he did not stop at this, but farcically pretended to take Polonius for a fishmonger, with much inconsequent talk about good kissing carrion (his notions are most unwholesome) and the *sun* breeding maggots in a dead dog.[1] And he then advised Polonius not to permit his daughter to walk in the *sun* and conceive. Why this preoccupation with the sun? Now I come to think of it, though his letter to Ophelia is not proved authentic, the sun figured in that as well. It is, of course, a vile pun and an equivocation between *sun* and *son*. Nor have I forgotten that at the first Council meeting, when I asked why the clouds still hung on him, he replied: 'Not so, my lord; I am too much in the *sun*.'

Finally, when Polonius most civilly asked to take his leave, the Prince rudely replied that there was nothing from which he would more willingly part withal, and called him a tedious old fool.

---

[1] *Translator's Note:* As this passage in the diary would be meaningless in literal translation, the translator has adopted the same words *sun* and *son* as did William Shakespeare, who was evidently faced with the same difficulty and found this solution for it, which can hardly be bettered.

All this leaves a most disagreeable taste. It is fortunate that Polonius has persuaded himself that Hamlet and his reason have parted company; otherwise I much fear this insolence could have done the old man a mortal injury.

22nd August

It is now ten days since that egregious pair, Rosencrantz and Guildenstern, were put to their task of 'taking Hamlet out of himself'. Precious little has as yet resulted from the experiment, though I hear tell of their introducing some players to the court. This should divert Hamlet, if anything will. But indeed I have little faith in the prescription, for already, it seems, Hamlet is set to teach them their business and he is like soon to tire of it, as will they.

I have Rosencrantz and Guildenstern under surveillance pursuant to a private instruction to Sigismund. It did not surprise me to learn that Hamlet at once surmised that they were acting under orders. It seems he contrived to place them off guard by greeting them as long-lost friends, and there was then some bawdy students' chat ('faith, her privates we'—*per* Guildenstern, and so forth); it is hard to believe that one enjoyed this sort of thing in days gone by! Then all of a sudden Hamlet turned on them and roundly accused them of being 'sent for' by the Queen and myself. We should have primed them for such an accusation; the boobies had no answer to it and looked (I am told) quite dazed.

Hamlet is certainly in a jumpy state. It amused me to read in the report that our luckless go-betweens were scolded for presuming to smile when Hamlet remarked that he took no delight in men—an unfortunate way of expressing himself. Thus nettled, he followed it up with the persistence of a neurotic dominie. 'Why did you laugh, then, when I said "man delights not me"?' Rosencrantz offered some lame excuse off the cuff, saying that in that case Hamlet would take no delight in the players, though why this should be a subject for merriment remains obscure. Of course it has been bruited about the court for years that Hamlet has eccentric tendencies. I do not credit it myself, but if he is so sensitive on the subject he would do better to refrain from indiscreet remarks. After all, there is nothing to be ashamed of: he is not being charged, as I am, with incest! [1]

23rd August

Polonius has tried his experiment and it has proved a total and painful failure. He and I bestowed ourselves in an adjoining room, within earshot. I saw nothing of the proceedings but heard more than enough to confirm me in my notion that Hamlet's treatment of Ophelia is—I know no word for it but *bestial*.

It became clear at once that Ophelia was determined to break with the Prince, for she asked him to accept the return of his love tokens. I was vastly relieved to hear it. And the more so to hear her say (did I mention that, demure as she is, she is a girl of spirit?) that 'rich gifts wax poor when givers prove unkind'. Doubtless irked by this, Hamlet progressed from sarcasm to fury and thence to a white passion of incoherence— a deplorable display, in face of which Ophelia remained calm and dignified. It has come to my mind more than once that she has both the courage and demeanour of a queen.

As for Hamlet, he ranted on about beauty transforming honesty to a bawd; though what in the name of reason this can mean is beyond my wits. He complained loudly of the ladies at court painting their faces and I know not what else. The unworthy thought struck me that perhaps those much abused playboys were right to snigger if Hamlet thinks this practice should be restricted to his own sex! He told her three or four times to go to a nunnery. On each occasion Polonius and I exchanged glances, I for my part (and he, doubtless, too) wondering if Ophelia would take the point. I judge that she did not, and indeed it is said with justice that to the pure all things are pure. It is outrageous that Hamlet should use such a word in Ophelia's presence, for it is no more than a cant term for a house of ill fame. He might as well have called her a trollop and had done with it.

---

[1] It is a popular theory amongst the pundits on sexual aberrations that horror of homosexuality and incest alternates down the ages. Shakespeare's plays limpidly reflect the Elizabethan toleration of the first and near-obsessive abomination of the second. The pendulum is close to a like point now and according to this theory will swing away again.—*Ed.*

I suspect that Hamlet was in part playing to the groundlings, as he so often does, that is to say to Polonius and myself. Both Polonius and Ophelia were put in a nice fix when Hamlet asked where Polonius was. Ophelia did what she could to protect her father, but made poor showing even with a white lie. As for Polonius, his features reflected the most ludicrous alarm. By the way, why should Hamlet have asked the question? The answer is simple if you know Hamlet: he had already made it his business to find out the answer. I will allow that Hamlet saved me the trouble of summing up the whole idiot business for the old man, doubly distressed by the humiliation of his daughter and the collapse of his plan. He did so most admirably, with the facility of a man in deep drink or frenzied anger, saying: 'Let the doors be shut upon him, that he may play the fool nowhere but in 's own house.' I could not have bettered it myself.

I wonder if Polonius noticed one self-revealing confession by Hamlet during this embarrassing encounter. Once again, my fatal verbal memory! 'I am very proud, revengeful, ambitious.' He did not repeat it, but I shall: *very proud, revengeful, ambitious.*

25th August

Is Hamlet mad? I ask myself this question again and again, but the answer is always the same. No, he is not. My reason tells me so; my bones tell me so. Then why does he feign madness? What could be less to the advantage of a prince, heir-presumptive to the throne?

Another question. Why has he rejected Ophelia? (I am not deluded by the outward form of things: her returning his love tokens was an effect, not a cause.) And why with so much contumely?

It is a mistake to ask too many questions at once. Hamlet has rejected Ophelia because she stands in the way of his dearest ambition. His dearest ambition is the throne. He is very proud, revengeful and ambitious. The throne offers him satisfaction in all three respects. What has Ophelia to do with this? She is the daughter of the chief minister now thwarting his designs, sister of Laertes, avowed enemy of the Primrose League. And he suspects that Polonius had a hand in the murder of his father, with what reason I know not; I have long since conceded that his secret service surpassed my own in a private station. All this talk of love is a declaration of self-love. And what young man, with any sense of propriety, would say to a girl that he 'loved her once'? As well say—I am tired of you now, I have other fish to fry.

Poor little Ophelia—my heart bleeds for her. Yet it would bleed more were she not now estranged from Hamlet. It is only the manner of the parting that I deprecate.

As for feigned madness, Hamlet has the most respectable of precedents, none other than the remorseless aspirant to another throne—King David. Is it possible that Hamlet goes in fear of me? I think not; he fears himself, the worst dread of all. Yet the analogy is just:

> And David arose and fled that day for fear of Saul, and went to Achish the king of Gath. And the servants of Achish said unto him, Is not this David the king of the land? Did they not sing one to another of him in dances, saying Saul hath slain his thousands, and David his ten thousands?
>
> And David laid up these words in his heart, and was sore afraid of Achish the king of Gath.
>
> And he changed his behaviour before them, and feigned himself mad in their hands, and scrabbled on the doors of the gate, and let his spittle fall down upon his beard.

And what was the outcome of it? He fled to the cave of Adullam and every one that was in distress and every one that was in debt, and every one that was discontented, gathered themselves unto him!

26th August

I have already remarked in so many words that Hamlet's rejection of Ophelia seems to be a natural consequence of his meddling in politics and itself a political move, though I concede that in all probability he begins to tire of her, so that his emotions are one with his purpose. Everything seems to point to this conclusion. And the brutality of his method— though nothing can excuse it—may be the more readily understood when it is put into perspective. What can it be but a reflection of his own sense of guilt? The more abominably he treats her, the greater is his sense of guilt and the more does he strain after supposed faults in her, hoping thereby to relieve his conscience. Yet the process but redoubles his tensions and I fear the more for Ophelia.

I judge that in my brother's lifetime Hamlet recognized that a match with Ophelia, though it might not be accounted brilliant, would please his mother, pass muster at the court and please the mob. All this remains true, but there are fresh considerations now. The circumstances of his father's death and my own accession have exacerbated the differences between Hamlet and Laertes and have consolidated the support which Polonius, by a natural gravitation, has always given to his son. It is not altogether surprising that the party of Laertes is now popularly known as 'the King's party'; I do nothing to countenance it but this is the inevitable consequence of Hamlet's opposition. Rightly or wrongly, Hamlet suspects that Polonius had a hand in the assassination of his father. With less reason he evidently thinks that I was also privy to it. Thus he finds himself in an untenable posture—courting the girl whose father he has always despised and now suspects of treachery and regicide, chief minister to his hated uncle!

These considerations, being largely emotional, must weigh much with Hamlet. But I judge that his decision to cut loose from Ophelia is dictated by a cooler and more rational calculation. He knows that he cannot effectively oppose the so-called King's party—which is to say that he cannot effectively pursue his treasonable designs against the State of Denmark, with or without the aid of Fortinbras—so long as it can be held against him that he is (to adopt his own coarse phrase) playing the fool in Polonius's house. Moreover he fears, and with good reason, that Polonius's house is bugged.

27th August

Did I mention that Penelope was lately appointed, at Gertrude's instance and with my approbation, principal lady-in-waiting to the Queen's bedchamber? The arrangement suits us all to perfection, and we have prevailed upon Stavridos to take up residence in the palace in my old quarters, which he now shares with his great-niece.

The move was a little delayed because Penelope declared that nothing would persuade her to move until the rooms had been redecorated to suit her own taste. This has now been done, at no small expense, but I must own that I should hardly recognize the place. I begin to wonder how I tolerated that bachelor suite for so many years.

At least I can take credit for the central heating, which Penelope tells me was the determinate feature in the old man's decision to move (he is now a martyr to arthritis, the curse of this humid climate). It is now working to admiration, though Penelope was inordinately vexed and more than a trifle outspoken when she discovered that several doors and windows were warped and were either stuck fast or would not close. It turns out that in an excess of zeal the Ministry of Works tried out the system on the hottest day of the summer, with spectacular results as many years' deposits of damp yielded to the treatment. It seems that Penelope came to inspect the new décor on this very day and she declares that the place was indistinguishable, in clouds of steam, from the palace laundry.

CHAPTER TWELVE

1st September

My birthday. Partridge shooting begins, as my nephew Hamlet
slyly remarked at the late King's last informal convention of
councillors. That piece of insolence serves to remind me that
on this very day his father should have returned to Elsinore,
flushed with victory and laden with the spoils—one knows not
what—of the short Norwegian campaign. Today I should have
relinquished my regency into more capable hands and retired
again to a private station.

How different is the reality. My brother dead, his wife my
consort, his son rebellious, his chief minister sliding into dotage,
his commander-in-chief under house arrest! And, worse, no
longer does Denmark threaten Norway: Norway, in the person
and gathering hordes of Fortinbras, threatens Denmark.

Having no relish for the ceremonial parade which traditionally marked the late King's birthday, I instituted instead
a training exercise on a large scale. This may serve in a small
measure to focus attention on the gravity of the Norwegian

crisis. There was some little grumbling about the innovation, but a donative of one extra day's pay for all ranks and a week's extra pay for signal initiative soon put an end to it.

I must own I have had a most enjoyable day, galloping about as chief umpire on a hypothetical battlefield, evolving situations of sudden and exacting predicament for our bovine commanders. The trouble is that our regular soldiers prefer the pedantry of the barrack-room to the discomfort of warfare. I well remember a gallant captain remarking sourly during the famous winter war that he hoped to be done with it soon and get back to 'proper soldiering'—that is to say, to manœuvres and parades!

The King's birthday banquet has also been eliminated from the calendar—ostensibly on the ground of economy in the public interest, actually because I see no reason to make a martyr of myself on my natal day. The Queen and I spent the evening very pleasantly as guests of the old doctor and Penelope. At least the greater part of the evening was pleasant. Penelope was amusing about my horoscope. It seems I was born under the sign of Virgo. It follows that I am by nature studious, orderly, analytical, somewhat secretive, etc. I need hardly state that Penelope was *not* born under the sign of Virgo; she is, I believe, a Sagittarian.

Alas, a cloud came over the company when I expounded my theory that Hamlet's rejection of Ophelia is part of a calculated design, an inevitable feature of his political manœuvring. The doctor's features remained immobile, but I detected a sympathetic exchange of glances between Gertrude and Penelope.

'Shall I tell him?' said Penelope, turning to the doctor.

The old man shrugged his shoulders, taciturn as ever.

'Shall I?' she said, turning to the Queen.

'As well that he should learn it from us as from others,' said the Queen.

There was a short silence while we looked at each other in turn. Then Gertrude said: 'I shall tell him, Penelope.'

She told me what it seems that they all know and have known for some days. Ophelia is *enceinte* by Hamlet. This she has disclosed, in her distress, to the Queen herself, and on the Queen's advice Stavridos has examined her. There can be no doubt of it.

These are evil tidings indeed. My heart is sore for Ophelia and hardened against Hamlet.

We did not discuss it at all but turned to other matters. The Queen and I took our leave soon afterwards.

17th September

I have been much occupied with affairs of State, which have left me no time for writing in my journal. I hear that the players are back and that Hamlet is diverting himself with them again, doubtless telling them how to go about their business. This is all to the good so long as it lasts. Less welcome is the news that we are all to endure the performance of a play which he is now rehearsing. This entertainment is to be presented to the court in about a fortnight's time. Personally I consider that a fortnight is excessive for rehearsals, but I have made it my business to find out that Hamlet is writing part of the play himself; this feature and his methods of production doubtless add to the delay.

I begin to ask myself whether Hamlet should not be banished from the court on some respectable pretext. Our original decision, much discussed with Gertrude, to prevent his return to Wittenberg, was shaped by the need to keep him under surveillance in the interests of the public safety. I confess his antics have made the process of surveillance odious to me, and this compels me to seek some other solution. The dangerous transitional period since the late King's death is now over; the change has been generally accepted and we are consolidated in the mastery of Denmark. Thus we can afford to relax precautions a little. Soon it will be four months[1] since the late King's untimely death—perhaps a short enough period for this process.

After the painful scene between Hamlet and Ophelia I suggested to Polonius that we might entrust Hamlet with a special mission to England for the demand of our neglected tribute. It is my notion that a change of scene might shake him out of his present brooding melancholy. (Moreover I

---

[1] Another instance of the accuracy of William Shakespeare. See Ophelia's correction of Hamlet's inaccuracy on the subject in the play scene (Act III, Sc. 2, 125): 'Nay, 'tis twice two months, my lord.'—*Ed.*

believe the climate there in the autumn is vile!) There should
be little opportunity for him to communicate with Fortinbras
once he is incarcerated in England. We can ill spare the tribute,
so sorely needed for our defensive armaments against Norway:
a pleasant thought that Hamlet would be engaged upon col-
lecting money for use against Fortinbras! Should he succeed
in the mission it may serve to restore his self-confidence (this
is a theory propounded by Stavridos; I see no lack of self-
confidence, myself). Should he fail, as I think more likely, it
will damage his credit with his own party and in Denmark at
large. Thus have I argued the case for his dispatch to England.
But in truth the argument is of little consequence, being sub-
sidiary to my compelling need to be spared the abiding nuisance
of his presence in the palace.

There was one fatal defect in the scheme: Polonius had not
thought of it himself! He temporized with the alternative
suggestion that Gertrude should first have a heart to heart
talk with her son. To this I have consented, for it is conceivable
that she may extract from him the true cause of his distemper.
And so it is arranged to take place after the play. It irks me to
wait until then, but it still seems faintly possible that Gertrude's
recipe of innocent diversion may effect a cure. Until then I
must possess my soul in patience.

26th September

Hamlet continues to divert himself with the players. Almost
am I persuaded that Gertrude's prescription is proving of some
avail. Yet such are the extremes of passion to which his temperament exposes him, I much fear that this tranquil spell
bodes ill.

Sigismund thoughtfully inquired whether I should wish to
receive the daily routine reports upon Hamlet's activities,
supposing perhaps that I should derive greater pleasure from
the play if I were not advised of its content in advance. I
suspect that his subordinates are becoming more than a trifle
fatigued with the rehearsals, which continue incessantly and
appear to be conducted for the most part in voices of a most
penetrating quality. To his evident annoyance I instructed him
to submit the reports as usual and to be sure to include full

details of our pleasure yet in store. Thus have I learnt that Hamlet has selected for the court's entertainment an obscure piece entitled *The Murder of Gonzago*, which he is at pains to tell everyone is written in very choice Italian. The relevance of this—if it be true—is obscure, as we shall presumably have to endure it in an indifferent translation!

I extracted a copy of this work from the palace library, but inasmuch as no translation was available, perforce I was obliged to make what I could of it in the very choice Italian, of which I am no judge. It is a pretentious story of melo-dramatic type. The scene is set in Vienna. (I have noticed, by the way, that playwrights gravitate by some process of natural selection to Vienna or Verona for their sillier plots; this of itself was enough to put me on suspicion.) A person called Lucianus murders a duke to gain possession of the duke's estate. A *non sequitur* one might suppose, for it has long been an established principle that a murderer is disqualified on intestacy. However, the author gets round this difficulty by marrying the assassin to the widowed duchess Baptista. Poor drama and worse law!

Whatever the merits of this play may be—and I can see none—I should be a dullard indeed did I fail to perceive the innuendo. Hamlet now seeks to advertise it to the court that his uncle is a murderer and his mother an accessory before the fact; whether or not she is also charged with adultery I cannot discover, but I put this down to my superficial acquaintance with the Italian tongue.

I have discussed the problem with Gertrude: I do not care to let it go further. My first impulse was to send the players packing. As I have already said, they are a noisy lot and I should be very well content to be rid of them. But, as Gertrude rightly remarks, some explanation should be offered for so doing, and it might be hard to contrive without thereby disclosing the security precautions of the palace. She pleads also for Hamlet's health, pointing to its improvement since he acquired this new interest. She fears that a sudden disruption of his much cherished plan to present this entertainment could undo all the good and expose him—and us also—to fresh outbursts of his erratic passions. Then, again, she says—and I must concur—that it will cause a great stir if I interdict the

play. Evil-minded persons may interpret it as an acknowledg-
ment of guilt, there will be sycophantic displays of sympathy
for Hamlet and we shall be making a martyr of him. Words
can break no bones, says Gertrude; we have nothing to do
but sit graciously through the performance!

These arguments are cogent, yet the proposal leaves me
uneasy. Were it not that I wish to humour Gertrude and am
loath to revive Hamlet's fevers, I should subordinate the reason
of the mind (that most fallible instrument) to the less fallible
reason of the marrow. I sense in my marrow that this bodes
ill. But grudgingly I agreed, for want of any alternative, that
the play be enacted. I have told Gertrude that I give Hamlet
the benefit of the doubt. I shall watch him narrowly: let him
overstep the mark and I shall conclude all as I think fit. The
cease of majesty dies not alone.

30th September

The play has proved an occasion of no small embarrassment,
ending in fiasco.

Hamlet was at his most febrile; I have learned to distrust
these euphoric moods. But I was determined to give him full
scope for the entertainment and to mark the occasion as one for
relaxed and innocent diversion. So at once after the Queen and I
had entered with Polonius, Ophelia and our attendant train, I
greeted Hamlet warmly, saying: 'How fares our cousin Hamlet?'
I had hoped that he might take the cue from this, but he replied
with extreme insolence: 'Excellent, i' faith; of the chameleon's
dish: I eat the air promise-crammed; you cannot feed capons so.'

Hamlet passes for a wit, and he has but to utter one of these
mannered and polished phrases to raise a titter from the
courtiers around him; they titter from custom and duty and
for fear that they may be accounted dullards if they do not
so advertise their comprehension of his drift. The usual sniggers
followed, but I doubt if any but Polonius and I understand
Hamlet; it is perhaps fortunate that he elects to express himself
in these turgid and obscure metaphors. Familiarity with his
atrocious puns makes all clear, a quibble on this occasion with
the words 'heir' and 'air'.[1] The purport of it is that he, the

[1] See footnote at p. 101 which applies, *mutatis mutandis.—Tr.*

heir to the throne, is being fed upon empty promises—an absurd proposition, for I have given him no promises. The reference to capons implies that he is being stuffed for killing! All this is unmannerly, unwarranted and ungracious. What is one to do with a young man in such a station who cannot comport himself with more discretion?

I replied, a little stiffly perhaps, but with the royal condescension born of habit: 'I have nothing with this answer, Hamlet.' He must know quite well what I meant by that. I flatter myself that the reply was apt, for most of the courtiers will have taken it to mean that I could not understand, any better than they, what he was talking about.

Hamlet then turned his attention to baiting Polonius, as is his wont, until I motioned to Rosencrantz to get the entertainment under way.

The Queen graciously invited Hamlet to sit at her side. He cannot be civil, even to his mother. 'Here 's metal more attractive,' he replied, throwing himself full length at the feet of Ophelia. To add to my mounting irritations Polonius could not let this pass without comment, asking me to mark it, presumably as evidence of Hamlet's obsessive passion for his daughter!

Now it was Ophelia's turn. My hearing is still acute and I could hear every word of their conversation against the general buzz. Knowing what I know now of their relationship and remembering how Ophelia had returned her love tokens and been roundly abused for her pains, I could not but be amazed by the colloquy. This is how it went:

Hamlet: Lady, shall I lie in your lap?
Ophelia: No, my lord.
Hamlet: I mean, my head upon your lap.
Ophelia: Ay, my lord.
Hamlet: Do you think I meant country matters?
(This is after his fashion, seeking to embroil her in his obscenities.)
Ophelia: I think nothing, my lord.
(Well said, say I.)
Hamlet: That 's a fair thought to lie between maids' legs.
Ophelia: What is, my lord?
Hamlet: Nothing.

Ophelia (distastefully): You are merry, my lord.
Hamlet: Who, I?
Ophelia: Ay, my lord.
Hamlet: O God, your only jig-maker. What should a man do but be merry? For look you, how cheerfully my mother looks, and my father died within's two hours.
Ophelia: Nay, 'tis twice two months, my lord.

And so it is, of course. What effrontery! I could see that Hamlet's sallies were as painful to Ophelia as was his easy assumption that he could continue to play the fool in this fashion after so lately abusing her to her face. I wish I could suppose that her glacial replies argue an indifference to Hamlet and his specious charms. I much fear that on the contrary she shows this brave face to the court because she has the natural dignity and courage of a queen. Within her lies a broken heart, a heart wantonly broken.

Next after this, though I affected to let it pass unnoticed, the players put on a dumb-show. This was, for me, the highlight of the evening, for several reasons. First, I could not fail to know (sedulous as has been Sigismund with his reports) that Hamlet has more than once expressed his detestation to the players of this silly and near obsolete stage practice. Secondly, I infer from his wishes being flouted that the players were minded to show, by their defiance, how much they resent his interference in their professional ploys. Thirdly, Hamlet was like to tear himself to pieces with rage at this deception of the players and apprehension lest I should turn from my conversation with the Queen to the theme of the dumb-show. In his vexation I heard him exclaim: 'Miching mallecho, this means mischief!' Even in anger he cannot spare us alliteration.

All this was high comedy indeed—not least this 'miching mallecho'—one of those slovenly phrases dear to the students of Wittenberg. Since these terms pass out of currency so soon as they have been done to death, I shall place it on record that *mallecho* is a Spanish word meaning wickedness and *miching* connotes a treacherous attack from the rear. An apt description, now I come to think of it, of this whole design of Hamlet's, for like a cur he tries to come at one, snapping, from behind.

Tedious as was the play, it would be more tedious to describe

I

it. Early enough I uttered a warning to Hamlet. Turning to him as the player king lay down to sleep in the garden—all too obviously a representation of my late brother and in deplorable taste—I said pointedly: 'Have you heard the argument? Is there no offence in 't?' He assured me there was none.

The player Lucianus soon came on stage and I kept a trifle of my attention on the play, the rest on Hamlet. Thus I could not fail to notice that, with the entry of Lucianus, Hamlet's *whole* attention was riveted on me and that of Horatio also. Soon other courtiers were beginning to stir and gape at myself and Gertrude. It is an old saw in Denmark that a cat may look at a king.

Ill-bred staring at the King and Queen by a body of persons acting in concert, and with the malicious design of putting them out of countenance, is a different proposition. Yet I still waited for that unmistakable sign of a deliberate and calculated affront, something which could not be attributed to the original text of *Gonzago* or explained away as coincidence. I did not have long to wait. Lucianus started to pour poison in the player king's ear. I scarce heard the doggerel which accompanied the action, though I assume it to be Hamlet's much pondered interpolation.

This was the sign. I rose at once, plucking Gertrude by the sleeve and called loudly for the lights. Insolence could scarce go further. The Queen and I retired, leaving the players and audience in disorder.

A dismal and disheartening experience; but instructive, most instructive.

IV

The Hectic in my Blood

CHAPTER THIRTEEN

5th October

I continue my journal from habit. It irks me that, as time goes on, I refer to my nephew Hamlet more often, more repetitively and less charitably. If, like a *spes successionis*, one can have an existence *in futuro*, I owe it to the unknown decoder of this journal—whose reality I yet assume—to explain, though I cannot condone this fault. In truth my journal is a reflection of myself: Hamlet becomes an obsession and I must watch myself, as—of necessity—I watch Hamlet.

So long as his father reigned, Hamlet was admittedly fractious, incalculable and wayward, even on occasions obstreperous—in a word, impish, with a devilry of impishness. But under his father's eye and mailed fist he had little scope to develop his talents or to wreak mischief on any grand scale. After his father's death he first fell into a brooding and sullen melancholy. Then there was the strange appearance of the ghost (or, as Polonius would have it, the less strange and more prosaic withdrawal of Ophelia's favours), upon which ensued a derangement of his reason or, as I believe, a simulated madness after the manner and precedent of that other notable

time-serving and self-seeking parvenu, King David. That was
the third phase. Then there was the fourth, of all too short a
duration, when he amused himself for a while—always with
mischievous intent—with the travelling players.

This last phase has been abruptly ended with the failure
of his childish *Gonzago* plot. What now? I am indebted to
Stavridos for an idiom, new to me, yet familiar to his colleagues
in Alexandria: the type of neurosis now brewing in Hamlet
is termed 'persecution mania'. I begin to wonder if I may not be
suffering from it myself. I suggested as much to Penelope and
Gertrude. The hilarity which this notion aroused has almost
persuaded me that this is a fancy.

Undated

> *Note:* Claudius's systematic methods seem to desert him at
> critical points in the narrative. The absence of date here is tire-
> some, for reasons which will appear later.
>   The text which follows treats of matters not previously
> mentioned: Claudius's religious faith and his sense of guilt
> con- cerning his brother's death. One asks if it is right to
> expose this part of the journal to the public gaze. The follow-
> ing reasons are advanced in support of the decision to include
> it: (*a*) that Claudius himself seems to imply, by his careful
> description of the palace quarters, that the text was intended
> for other eyes; (*b*) that in no other way is it possible to disabuse
> the public of prejudices implanted by William Shakespeare's
> interpretation of the scene which follows; and (*c*) that the
> mounting tension between Claudius and Hamlet would be
> inexplicable if the scene were, with more scruple, suppressed.
> —*Ed.*

Last night before retiring I entered my closet to pray, as I
always do. This, with the antechamber which separates it from
the corridor, was used by the late King as a dressing-room,
his requirements in that respect being less exacting than my
own. There are three methods of access to the closet—on either
hand from the Queen's bedroom and my own through archways flanked with heavy draperies, or by the door to the
antechamber. My Switzers are posted about this wing of the
palace at such vantage points that they may keep every door
under observation, except for one. I do not care to be observed at
prayer; thus the King's Closet (as it is known) is left unobserved.

I have my prie-dieu set up in this closet at the far end, beneath a cheval mirror used by my late brother. Thus, as I kneel, I have my back to the antechamber; on either side and a little behind me are the two archways to the bedrooms.

All this I mention because it might otherwise be hard to understand what I now relate: the most unnerving experience of a life not empty of sudden shocks, predicaments, night sweats and dangers.

Lately I have sought heavenly grace for long hours at my prie-dieu, little thinking that any but Gertrude could know of it. My brother's murder weighs heavily upon me. *Per facit per alium facit per se.* My reason tells me that I am no accessory before the fact, for I had no knowledge of the design, no certainty of its execution, no acquaintance with the means. But of what worth is reason? It is not reason but my actions, tried by the test of conscience, that I must submit to my Maker. I bear the heavy burden of that *suspicion*, already bred in my brother's lifetime, that his life was threatened. Yet I was content to let matters take their course; vacillating, I uttered empty warnings, but none to him.

Thus do I pray, long and earnestly, for grace. Yet my offence is rank; it smells to heaven. It has the primal, eldest curse upon it—a brother's murder! Pray can I not, though inclination be as sharp as will. The crown oppresses and chafes me as it did before my coronation in that memorable nightmare. My words fly up; my thoughts remain below.

Although, as I have said, my hearing is acute, I heard no sound to warn me that Hamlet had entered the antechamber. I cannot judge how long he had been standing there before I became aware of his presence. It is wrong to suppose that we have but five senses: to these must be added that sensory perception, so fully developed in the blind and in animals, the perception of something or someone being *there*. This sense is most acute at night and in moments of extreme danger.

Warned by this sense, I raised my eyes a little to the cheval mirror, which reflected the figure of Hamlet standing in the shadows of the antechamber, his rapier drawn from the scabbard. His face was illumined by the steady light of the two wax candles which stand in their silver sconces on either side of the prie-dieu. Upon it was limned an expression of indescribable savagery.

I confess I was frozen with fear, unarmed as I was, without so much as a dagger at my side. It was evident he had only to take seven quick paces to run me through. I continued to kneel. And to pray.

Then, after what seemed an eternity, I was conscious of something else: Hamlet speaking to himself in an undertone. It is said that soliloquy is the first sign of madness. I do not believe it: rather, say, it is a symptom of irredeemable mania. Hamlet seemed unaware that he spoke at all. It is with some difficulty that I express my meaning: speech was not the vehicle of his thoughts, but a casual effect—the forcing from him of speech as may be observed in a sleep walker. And all the more horrible. Every word he spoke is engraved in my memory. Nothing has yet been unfit to enter in my journal, but for this I must make exception. Let the memory of these words remain with Hamlet and me alone. I cannot bring myself to set them down.

[*Note:* Here Claudius abruptly breaks off his account of the prayer scene, leaving us in doubt what happened next. For want of other evidence of what, precisely, Hamlet said which so much shocked his uncle, there is reproduced below the speech as it appears in William Shakespeare's stage version of the story:

Hamlet:

Now might I do it pat, now he is praying;
And now I 'll do 't: and so he goes to heaven;
And so am I reveng'd. That would be scann'd:
A villain kills my father; and for that,
I, his sole son, do this same villain send
To heaven,
Why, this is hire and salary, not revenge.
He took my father grossly, full of bread,
With all his crimes broad blown, as flush as May;
And how his audit stands who knows save heaven?
But in our circumstance and course of thought
'Tis heavy with him. And am I then reveng'd,
To take him in the purging of his soul,
When he is fit and season'd for the passage?
No.

Up, sword, and know thou a more horrid hent;
When he is drunk asleep, or in his rage,
Or in the incestuous pleasure of his bed,
At gaming, swearing, or about some act
That has no relish of salvation in 't;
Then trip him, that his heels may kick at heaven,
And that his soul may be as damn'd and black
As hell, whereto it goes. . . .]

CHAPTER FOURTEEN

Note: The prayer scene described in the preceding pages was evidently separated from the bedroom scene by an interval of two or three days. So much is apparent from Claudius's own text. But the point needs to be stressed, for if it were not so Claudius would surely be carrying chronology to a pedantic extreme in describing the prayer scene first and the far more calamitous bedroom scene later. And if these events had all occurred on the same night, one cannot but suppose—bearing in mind the arrangement of the royal apartments so minutely described by Claudius in the prayer scene—that he would have been within earshot of those cries for help uttered by Gertrude and Polonius.

Close familiarity with William Shakespeare's stagecraft and artistic licence should not be allowed to eclipse the facts nor blind us to the improbability of these events occurring in immediate sequence. W. S. carries us along at such a pace that we do not have time to ask how it came about that, so soon after Claudius had been put in mortal fear of his own life, he heard nothing of the considerable commotion in the Queen's bedroom but had to ask the Queen for an account of it afterwards. (And this, despite his telling us several times that his hearing was acute—perhaps an excusable foible?) Nor why, knowing that

the Prince had paused in the antechamber on his way to answer
the Queen's summons, and recognizing his ugly mood, he took
no extra precautions for the Queen's safety. This is not in
character.

All becomes plain when it is realized that the ordeals of the
King and Queen did *not* take place on the same night. It was
fundamental to the scheme devised by Polonius that the Queen
should sound Hamlet by herself and in *seeming* privacy (eaves-
dropped only by Polonius himself). Thus it is a fair inference
that on *that* night Claudius placed himself well out of the way,
which, as things turned out, was just as well for him. Thus he
would have known nothing of the events in the Queen's apartment until he was called to the scene to hear Gertrude's breath-
less account of it. *Vide* Act IV, Sc. 1, lines 1 and 2: 'There's
matter in these sighs, these profound heaves: you must trans-
late; 'tis fit we understand them.'—*Ed.*

12th October

My soul is full of discord and dismay. Hamlet has murdered
Polonius. This violence was presaged as I knelt at prayer but
two or three nights since, yet I placed no restraint upon the
Prince. Now is this dreadful crime added to the insupportable
burden of my conscience. Worse—the Queen, a hapless witness
of this bloody murder, judges from Hamlet's ravings, as do I,
that Hamlet mistook the poor old man for me. This was the
last service of Polonius to the State of Denmark. I salute him
in awe and gratitude.

The Queen's ordeal has been fearful. I will try to set down
what she has related to me.

Hamlet came to her apartment upon her summons, Polonius
being concealed behind the arras. She says that from the outset
Hamlet's demeanour was haughty and contemptuous. 'Now,
mother, what's the matter?' was his greeting.

Gertrude, perhaps unwisely, pleaded with him to be less
aggressive in his dealings with me, saying that he had much
offended me. This put him in a passion of resentment. He
heaped reproaches on his mother for—as he put it—offending
his father, and chided her for her second marriage. Then he
forced her to be seated and announced that she should not
budge until he had done with reviewing her sins.

Hamlet's behaviour and visage were so threatening that
Gertrude says she was terrified; she was convinced that he was

minded to murder her. How should I blame her for this when I have so lately been threatened likewise? In her anguish she cried out for help; Polonius, from behind the arras, doubtless seized by the same fear, cried out also. Whereupon Hamlet whipped out his rapier and ran him through. As the old man slumped to the floor—this is appalling—Hamlet remarked in a casual manner that he did not know who it might be—was it the King? Then, lifting up the arras and finding there the body of Polonius, he heaped reproaches this time on the corpse: 'Thou wretched, rash, intruding fool.' And then: 'I took thee for thy better.' Unmistakable evidence of his disappointment and intent to murder me! This is indeed cold-blooded, horrible.

For the rest I must credit what the Queen has told me, unbelievable as it is. With the blood-stained corpse lying huddled on the floor, Hamlet resumes his verbal assault on his mother with redoubled violence, as though it were no more than a tiresome distraction of the moment to assassinate the King's chief minister. Even so, Gertrude, resigned to fate and with that spirit that I so much admire in her, spoke up and said (I can well believe it):

> What have I done that thou dar'st wag thy tongue
> In noise so rude against me?

But it was useless. Hamlet was determined to express the poison from his system. If he uttered one tenth of what she has related to me he is indeed sick in his mind. At length the Queen was prepared to make any confession or vow to humour him. I applaud her decision. This is the way to deal with a maniac. Yet it was of no avail. As will appear, the Queen was saved by the very fever of Hamlet's brain conjuring up supernatural intervention.

A sample of Hamlet's ranting, as the Queen cited it to me, struck me as in character, nor is Gertrude capable of fabricating such phrases: 'Nay, but to live in the rank sweat of an enseaméd bed, stew'd in corruption, honeying and making love over the nasty sty.' Well, well! I should like to know, by the way, why the young so preposterously assume that it is their exclusive privilege to avail themselves of the natural attraction of the sexes, so providentially dispensed for the solace of mankind. Generally speaking they know so little about it and practise it in such a clumsy fashion! I gather that Hamlet expressed himself on this subject in his customary ornate but shallow manner, declaring that at his mother's age the heyday in the blood is tame, it's humble and waits upon the judgment, etc., though indeed I do not know why it should be the worse for that: I detect in all this more than a trace of his shame for having got Ophelia with child. Not his fault, again.

Now this is the most bizarre part of the whole story. Hamlet was still lecturing his mother and comparing my qualities (not to my advantage) with those of his father, when all of a sudden he broke off his monologue and addressed himself to emptiness —or, as Gertrude most vividly expressed it, 'held discourse with the incorporal air'. There ensued long intervals of silence, while Hamlet gazed steadfastly at one or another point of the compass, unmindful of his mother, except occasionally, as when he turned to her and said: 'How is it with you, lady?' To this she replied, with some justice: 'Alas, how is 't with *you*?'

This part of the business was most strange and has convinced the Queen, as nothing else has done, that her son is mad. From time to time he seemed to be describing to Gertrude what he saw, or thought he saw—that is to say, his father, in his habit as he lived. In brief, as I infer, it is another visitation of the ghost. It is a most persistent ghost. Moreover there is one point on which I must agree with Hamlet: it is an honest ghost. Gertrude is indebted to it, or him (I am not entirely clear about the sex of spectres) for the preservation of her life.

After a while this honest ghost took his (or its) leave, Gertrude doing her best, though unsuccessfully, to observe its (his) departure through the doorway. Then, after another but less threatening sermon from Hamlet, and some prudent if ingratiating remarks from Gertrude, Hamlet also took his leave, removing with him the sad remains of poor old Polonius. 'I 'll lug the guts into the neighbour room. Mother, good night!' I find it particularly unpleasant that the neighbouring room is my little prayer closet which lies alongside.

Though Gertrude, after this harrowing experience, is evidently now persuaded that her son is mad, I cannot concur. It is one thing to be mad, quite another to be a cool, shrewd and calculating maniac.

Undated

I have had no stomach to complete the task of setting down the events of that awful night. Now Hamlet has been taken care of and Polonius has been laid to rest, I feel a little calmer and shall do it.

By the time I had been summoned to the Queen's apartments, accompanied by Rosencrantz and Guildenstern, Hamlet had disappeared and so had the body of Polonius. By the Queen's account Hamlet had gone to drag the body away from the King's Closet and was then weeping for what he had done. This show of remorse she accounts to his credit, but I find it nauseating.

I dispatched Rosencrantz and Guildenstern at once to find the body and bring Hamlet before me. Even at this crisis Hamlet could not forbear to sharpen his wits on the pair, to no purpose but to waste precious time. After a while Rosencrantz—showing, for once, some presence of mind in leaving Guildenstern to watch Hamlet—returned to say that Hamlet would not disclose where he had bestowed the body. At my command Guildenstern then brought Hamlet before me.

Hamlet's demeanour was unashamedly brazen. I demanded that he tell me what he had done with Polonius. He replied that Polonius was at supper—being supped by worms. With mounting impatience I endured a lengthy discourse upon this unpleasant theme, leading to the conclusion that a king—and a prince, I might remark also—may go a progress through the guts of a beggar. Such is the unwholesome cast of his mind, dwelling upon sun-kissing carrion, graveyard worms and the like. I cut him short, repeating the question: where is Polonius? He cringes at once upon a frontal assault, true to his nature of a miching mallecho. He had hidden the body up a staircase leading to a lobby. I did not trouble to ask why; his actions are not always those of an adult.

The long and the short of it is that I have embarked him in all haste for England. He set sail the same night. As the project has been under discussion for some time past it was no great surprise to him. I explained that this unspeakable crime left me with no alternative but to put the plan into immediate execution for his own safety. He tried to brazen this out as well, affecting to receive the news with satisfaction. 'Good,' he said, to which I replied: 'So is it, if thou knew'st our purposes.'

Do it, England; for like the hectic in my blood he rages.

CHAPTER FIFTEEN

22nd October

But five short months ago I supposed—may God forgive me—
that my life might be easier and sweeter were I spared the
leaden oppression of my brother Hamlet. Ten days ago I
supposed that, with my nephew Hamlet banished, Gertrude
and I might at last enjoy an Indian summer, a long-deferred
peace of mind. I confess I thought we had both reached the
very frontier of human endurance. What a folly of surmise!
As I have lately remarked to Gertrude, when sorrows come
they come not single spies but in battalions. Not long since we
seemed secure upon the throne. Now all is once more awry.

Hamlet's abrupt departure has aroused much speculation
and has been generally and ignorantly censured. The dis-
tracted multitude ever weigh the offender's scourge but never
the offence. Worse, we dare not divulge the offence. Hamlet is
in an impregnable position; he knows, as do Gertrude and I,
that if he were generally supposed guilty of the murder, it

might bring down the whole royal family. And the mob will believe what they wish to believe.

As for Polonius, it was given out that he had suffered a sudden and fatal stroke—a macabre thought that this, in another sense, is true! Few believe it. With the people muddied, thick and unwholesome in their thoughts and whispers, a State funeral, such as the old man had so richly deserved, was clearly an act of unthinkable rashness. The King's party (how long will it remain such?) were already accusing the Primrose League of complicity in the murder, and seeing that Hamlet was the author of this crime, with more reason than they knew. Incensed by these accusations and shaken by Hamlet's mysterious and sudden disappearance, the Primrose League, in turn, were accusing the King's party of assassinating Hamlet. Thus did we decide in hugger-mugger to inter our chief minister. I console myself in the knowledge that his infallible sense of accord with public sentiment and of the practicable would have approved the decision, even if the arguments for and against it were not developed, in his inevitable absence, so thoroughly as he might have wished.

These reflections weigh heavily upon me, but it is my lot and duty to bear the burdens of Denmark. It is a catastrophe of another order, so unforeseen, so cruel, which I find nearly insupportable; this is the unmistakable malice of fate. My lovely Ophelia, crushed by Hamlet's intolerance and her adored father's death, has gone out of her mind. At least, for this we cannot reproach ourselves. Gertrude has ever loved her as a daughter. Her first act was to bring Ophelia into our private apartments, and since her father died she has lived with us in care and tenderness.

But it has been of no avail.

Today, to my infinite distress, I found Ophelia singing her little ditties to the Queen, interspersing little inconsequent comments in a manner which could leave no doubt of her sad derangement. I affected to notice nothing and spoke to her gently as I always do. She spoke wild words and then broke again into song. I am above all distressed by her liberation from all sense of propriety; the conventions which she has so sedulously observed according to her father's precepts no longer exist for her. Did I say that to the pure all things are

K

pure? Yes, and I believe it still of Ophelia. Think ill of the fever, not of the patient. Yet it was hard to endure her songs, so unbecoming and out of character, so pathetic:

> Then up he rose and donn'd his clothes,
>   And dupp'd the chamber door;
> Let in the maid, that out a maid
>   Never departed more.

What is this, I ask myself, but Hamlet again? I could not find words to express nor to conceal my heaviness. 'Pretty Ophelia!' I said, and to this she replied, after the manner of any strumpet: 'Indeed, la! without an oath, I 'll make an end on 't', and resumed her singing:

> By Gis and by Saint Charity
>   Alack, and fie for shame!
> Young men will do 't, if they come to 't;
>   By Cock they are to blame.
>
> Quoth she, before you tumbled me,
>   You promis'd me to wed:

And then, in a fantastical imitation of Hamlet, who has neither ear nor voice:

> So would I ha' done, by yonder sun,
>   An thou hadst not come to my bed.

Gertrude tells me that, before I entered the room, Ophelia had sung 'How should I your true love know from another one?', which both of us remembered so well from that evening when Hamlet accompanied her on his recorder. I do not think I could have borne this.

25th October

Immediately after the sudden death of Polonius I recalled Laertes from Paris, but it was plainly impossible for him to attend his father's funeral. I had long since resolved to advance Laertes upon his father's death or retirement from public affairs, not only because of his sterling qualities but because there is no other leader for a party implacably opposed to that of Hamlet.

I confess that the collapse of Ophelia's reason has for the

last two days obliterated all else from my mind save the fearful prospect of communicating these tidings to her brother on his return. But as so often happens the reality proved utterly different from the expectation—in some ways better, in others worse.

I write this on the day after the return of Laertes. What has Sigismund been about that I received no warning of his attempt to storm the palace—an attempt, I may say, in which he wholly succeeded? A fine greeting from my chief minister designate! But I run ahead of myself and must try to give a more orderly account of this affair, in which I really believe that the Queen and I were within a hair's breadth of assassination. We were talking together quietly in our apartments when there was a loud disturbance without. I had time for nothing but to shout for my Switzers. A gentleman of my train at once burst in and advised us to flee, saying that Laertes had irrupted into the palace with a rabble at his heels, chanting—though indeed by this time I could hear them—that Laertes should be king.

The Queen with great spirit rose from her embroidery and at once disabused him of any notion that we might act on his recommendation. I could see she was ready to discharge a stupendous stream of invective at the mob, but she had got no further than 'false Danish dogs' when Laertes himself appeared in the doorway. The Queen then interposed herself between him and me, trying to pinion him—an act of signal courage.

Laertes, the while, though impeded by the Queen before him and the rabble at his back, was in course of uttering incoherent revilements and accusations, the drift of which, none the less, was unmistakable. He has more courage than Hamlet but less command of speech.

There are moments, rare enough, when I know myself to be Denmark, not Claudius. I commanded Gertrude to let go of Laertes and stood there silent before him, unarmed. The rabble, awed by the presence of the King or awaiting the fatal stroke—I know not which—also fell silent. I addressed myself with icy contempt of them to Gertrude:

> Let him go, Gertrude; do not fear our person:
> There's such divinity doth hedge a king,
> That treason can but peep to what it would. . . .

Then I commanded Laertes to speak. He asked in a shame-faced manner where his father was. I answered in a single word, 'Dead'. The Queen foolishly interposed 'But not by him'. Unfortunately she has more courage than sense. I cut her short, saying curtly:

'Let him demand his fill.'

This was the crucial moment. Laertes floundered on to his conclusion that he sought revenge for the death of his father. By now the mob were weary of the discussion.

'Who shall stay you?' I replied. I knew who was the master now. Short of some foolish provocation by Gertrude we should sleep in our beds again.

Then I put it to him—did he genuinely seek revenge for his father's death or was this but a pretext for uniting the kingdom against me? Did he in all sincerity seek out his father's enemies?

Doubtless Hamlet would have found some evasive reply, but Laertes is not of such stuff. He replied, and I knew it to be true, that he sought none but his father's enemies. Once again he looked shamefaced. He is no regicide. I drew him to me for closer and more intimate discussion. The mob melted away.

It was as well that it all happened thus, for Ophelia, disturbed, I must suppose, by the unprecedented noise, entered the apartment soon after these exchanges and to my dismay poor Laertes was confronted with his sister before we had time to prepare him for the encounter. Ophelia sang more ditties, dwelling for ever on her father's death.

> He never will come again.
> His beard was as white as snow
> All flaxen was his poll.
>   He is gone, he is gone. . . .

I drew Laertes aside. We had much to speak of.

CHAPTER SIXTEEN

28th October

For some little time past there have been strange rumours abroad that Hamlet had set foot in Denmark again, but I have paid no attention to them. It was the same when the late King was murdered: he was expected to return at any moment (to what extent the wish was father to his ghost, none can be sure). It was by chance as I sat closeted with Laertes on State business that the fateful message arrived:

> High and mighty, you shall know I am set naked on your kingdom. Tomorrow shall I beg leave to see your kingly eyes; when I shall, first asking your pardon thereunto, recount the occasions of my sudden and more strange return.
> Hamlet

At first I took it for a forgery. But though the handwriting might be counterfeit, I defy anyone to perfect the illiterate insolence of Hamlet's style. And in a postscript he writes the one word 'Alone'. None but Hamlet could invest this solitary word with so many and threatening undertones. Plainly he has by some contrivance escaped the vessel carrying him to England and is again in Denmark to stir up trouble. This stress upon 'naked' and 'alone' is no cry for compassion on his fate—by no means! It is as much as to say: Now that I have thrown off your captors, I come into my own and you may look to your safety. So be it, Hamlet: the King shall for once adopt your counsel.

29th October

How much I had to do to calm the rage of Laertes! At last I convinced him that Hamlet had been pursuing my own life when by mischance he slew Polonius. Why, he asked, did I not proceed against Hamlet by due process of law? I explained what should have been obvious. First, despite all, Gertrude still dotes upon Hamlet, no matter that she fears him too. Secondly, by so doing, we should have put the crown in jeopardy, for the mob will have nothing said against him. In no time at all they would have converted his gyves to graces. We could not, in other words, accept the risk of making a martyr of him.

All this, by slow degrees, I communicated to Laertes. How different from his father, whose lively apprehension grasped the thought before it had been fully shaped, sometimes before it had been uttered! But no matter, Laertes is all solid worth; there are tasks for which one may prefer a cart-horse.

In the end it was done and he has accepted to be ruled by me in every respect but one, for I am to allow him liberty to revenge himself upon Hamlet. His father's death and his sister's madness have persuaded me to this concession. He talked loud of revenge, with such crude fancies as cutting Hamlet's throat in the church. When Hamlet rages, which is often, his wits become sharpened to a razor's edge. It is to the credit of Laertes that his are dulled to absurdity. I can but suppose that, in his muddled thinking, the more abominable the crime, the greater the vengeance! It is one of my besetting sins that I cannot refrain from acid comments which nobody can understand. I remarked that no place indeed should murder sanctuarize. I commit it to my journal, for clearly it made no sense to Laertes.

30th October

I have given much thought to Hamlet's letter and have considered it in conjunction with reports now submitted to me
by Sigismund that Hamlet *is* in Denmark and is being followed. It is plain that there is not the faintest prospect of his
arriving here in the palace for several days. So much for his
'tomorrow'—but for this relief much thanks. I am told that
Hamlet has given it out that the vessel was boarded by pirates
and that he escaped in the tussle. The story is improbable in
itself and the circumstance that Hamlet has given it currency
is prima facie evidence of its falsehood. All the evidence points
to the vessel having been boarded, it is true, but not by pirates.
That is to say, not by pirates in the accepted sense of the word.
This is nothing more nor less than a rescue operation, put into
effect with great skill and contrivance by a man-of-war com-
missioned by Fortinbras. So much we know.

Is it a coincidence that Fortinbras now renews his request
for a safe conduct for himself and his armed rabble through
our domain?

1st November

Affairs of State and multiple anxieties do so press upon me that
it seems I must soon relinquish my journal to this merciless
tension. Already I sense a loss of sequence, of orderly arrangement. This is anathema to me. I ask myself, what can be the
purpose or usefulness of a journal in which everything is not
set down in its right order and sequence? This sort of confusion
is the mark of the muddled witness, the hallmark of idle and
careless thought. Had I time I should correct the fault.

To these comments I am moved by the discovery that I have
failed to mention—doubtless in my concern with the news of
Hamlet's impending return (he has not arrived yet—unpunctual
as ever!)—that, after the disturbance in our private apartments
a week ago, I judged the palace to be unsafe for Gertrude and
Ophelia and prevailed with difficulty upon Gertrude to take
Ophelia to my country retreat. My apprehensions concerning
the security of the palace would have been the worst of arguments to advance to Gertrude, whose foreign blood still boils
at those 'Danish dogs' and the damage they have done to the

palace furnishings. No matter—it falls to my inevitable lot to advance specious arguments for the right causes. Eventually with some small assistance from Stavridos I persuaded her that it was inadvisable that Ophelia be exposed to the daily hubbub of Elsinore and that both of them could profit from a change of scene. At that time I did not know that there was this threat of Hamlet's return, but when I did learn of it I was thankful to providence for inspiring me with this thought, for Ophelia will be out of the way when he returns.

11th November

Gertrude has returned with tidings which so wring my heart that I can scarce set them down: little Ophelia is drowned. Thus do all our care and compassion come to naught. Drowned in a little brook, a haunt of my childhood, in the early hours of the morning with the dew yet on the grass—singing, I cannot doubt it, her little lauds in her true, clear voice, unknown to Gertrude and Sussi, whose watchfulness and love for her were those of a mother and nurse.

Gertrude is again distraught, so also Laertes. It falls to me to exert sovereignty against the one power, Hamlet excepted, which can effectively oppose it—the Church. They would have her buried at a crossroads with a suicide's stake. . . . This is Christian charity indeed!

With much labour I achieved a compromise: she shall be buried in Christian burial and in consecrated ground. Dear Ophelia, they say they will deny you more, for a requiem would profane the service of the dead. In this, as in all else, I have failed. Forgive me.

Note: This is the final entry in the diary of Claudius. The rest is silence, except for Shakespeare's account of the sequel, reprinted here for the convenience and interest of readers who may have followed Claudius so far. In view of the many hints by Claudius that Hamlet was in league with Fortinbras, nothing is perhaps of greater interest in this text than Hamlet's words: 'I do prophesy the election lights on Fortinbras: he has my dying voice.'—*Ed.*

EPILOGUE

From the play by William Shakespeare
entitled *Hamlet, Prince of Denmark*

Enter a Lord.

Lord. My lord, his majesty commended him to you by young Osric, who brings back to him, that you attend him in the hall; he sends to know if your pleasure hold to play with Laertes, or that you will take longer time.

Hamlet. I am constant to my purposes; they follow the King's pleasure: if his fitness speaks, mine is ready; now or whensoever, provided I be so able as now.

Lord. The king, and queen, and all are coming down.

Hamlet. In happy time.

Lord. The queen desires you to use some gentle entertainment to Laertes before you fall to play.

Hamlet. She well instructs me.   [*Exit* Lord.

Horatio. You will lose this wager, my lord.

Hamlet. I do not think so; since he went into France, I have been in continual practice; I shall win at the odds. But thou wouldst not think how ill all 's here about my heart; but it is no matter.

Horatio. Nay, good my lord——

Hamlet. It is but foolery; but it is such a kind of gain-giving as would perhaps trouble a woman.

Horatio. If your mind dislike any thing, obey it; I will forestal their repair hither, and say you are not fit.

Hamlet. Not a whit, we defy augury; there's a special providence in the fall of a sparrow. If it be now, 'tis not to come; if it be not to come, it will be now; if it be not now, yet it will come: the readiness is all. Since no man has aught of what he leaves, what is 't to leave betime? Let be.

Enter KING, QUEEN, LAERTES, Lords, OSRIC *and* Attendants *with foils, etc.*

King. Come, Hamlet, come, and take this hand from me.

[*The* KING *puts the hand of* LAERTES *into that of* HAMLET.

139

Hamlet. Give me your pardon, sir; I 've done you wrong;
But pardon 't, as you are a gentleman.
This presence knows, and you must needs have heard,
How I am punished with a sore distraction.
What I have done
That might your nature, honour and exception
Roughly awake, I hear proclaim was madness.
Was 't Hamlet wrong'd Laertes? Never Hamlet:
If Hamlet from himself be ta'en away,
And when he 's not himself does wrong Laertes,
Then Hamlet does it not; Hamlet denies it.
Who does it then? His madness. If 't be so,
Hamlet is of the faction that is wrong'd;
His madness is poor Hamlet's enemy.
Sir, in this audience,
Let my disclaiming from a purpos'd evil
Free me so far in your most generous thoughts,
That I have shot mine arrow o'er the house,
And hurt my brother.

Laertes.   I am satisfied in nature,
Whose motive, in this case, should stir me most
To my revenge; but in my terms of honour
I stand aloof, and will no reconcilement,
Till by some elder masters, of known honour,
I have a voice and precedent of peace,
To keep my name ungor'd. But till that time,
I do receive your offer'd love like love,
And will not wrong it.

Hamlet.   I embrace it freely;
And will this brother's wager frankly play.
Give us the foils. Come on.

Laertes.   Come, one for me.

Hamlet. I 'll be your foil, Laertes; in mine ignorance
Your skill shall, like a star i' the darkest night,
Stick fiery off indeed.

Laertes.   You mock me, sir.

Hamlet. No, by this hand.

King. Give them the foils, young Osric. Cousin Hamlet,
You know the wager?

Hamlet.   Very well, my lord;
Your Grace hath laid the odds o' the weaker side.

King. I do not fear it; I have seen you both;
But since he is better'd, we have therefore odds.

Laertes. This is too heavy; let me see another.

Hamlet. This likes me well. These foils have all a length?

Osric. Ay, my good lord.   [*They prepare to play.*

King. Set me the stoups of wine upon that table.
  If Hamlet give the first or second hit,
  Or quit in answer of the third exchange,
  Let all the battlements their ordnance fire;
  The king shall drink to Hamlet's better breath;
  And in the cup an union shall he throw,
  Richer than that which four successive kings
  In Denmark's crown have worn. Give me the cups;
  And let the kettle to the trumpet speak,
  The trumpet to the cannoneer without,
  The cannons to the heavens, the heavens to earth,
  'Now the king drinks to Hamlet!' Come, begin;
  And you, the judges, bear a wary eye.

Hamlet. Come on, sir.

Laertes.   Come, my lord.   [*They play.*

Hamlet.   One.

Laertes.   No.

Hamlet.   Judgment.

Osric. A hit, a very palpable hit.

Laertes.   Well; again.

King. Stay; give me drink. Hamlet, this pearl is thine;
  Here's to thy health. Give him the cup.
                    [*Trumpets sound; and cannon shot off within.*

Hamlet. I 'll play this bout first; set it by awhile.
  Come. [*They play*]. Another hit; what say you?

Laertes. A touch, a touch, I do confess.

King. Our son shall win.

Queen.   He 's fat, and scant of breath.
  Here, Hamlet, take my napkin, rub thy brows;
  The queen carouses to thy fortune, Hamlet.

Hamlet. Good madam!

King. Gertrude, do not drink.

Queen. I will, my lord; I pray you, pardon me.

King. [*Aside.*] It is the poison'd cup! It is too late.

Hamlet. I dare not drink yet, madam; by and by.

Queen. Come, let me wipe thy face.

Laertes. My lord, I 'll hit him now.

King.   I do not think 't.

Laertes. [*Aside.*] And yet 'tis almost 'gainst my conscience.

Hamlet. Come for the third, Laertes. You but dally;
    I pray you, pass with your best violence.
    I am afeard you make a wanton of me.
Laertes. Say you so? Come on.   [*They play.*
Osric. Nothing, neither way.
Laertes. Have at you, now.
       [LAERTES *wounds* HAMLET; *then, in scuffling, they change rapiers,*
        and HAMLET *wounds* LAERTES.
King. Part them! they are incens'd.
Hamlet. Nay, come again.   [*The* QUEEN *falls.*
Osric.   Look to the queen there, ho!
Horatio. They bleed on both sides. How is it, my lord?
Osric. How is it, Laertes?
Laertes. Why, as a woodcock to mine own springe, Osric;
    I am justly kill'd with mine own treachery.
Hamlet. How does the queen?
King.   She swounds to see them bleed.
Queen. No, no, the drink, the drink—O my dear Hamlet!
    The drink, the drink; I am poison'd.   [*Dies.*
Hamlet. O villany! Ho! let the door be lock'd:
    Treachery! seek it out.
Laertes. It is here, Hamlet. Hamlet, thou art slain;
    No medicine in the world can do thee good;
    In thee there is not half an hour of life;
    The treacherous instrument is in thy hand,
    Unbated and envenom'd. The foul practice
    Hath turn'd itself on me; lo! here I lie,
    Never to rise again. Thy mother's poison'd.
    I can no more. The king, the king's to blame.
Hamlet. The point envenom'd too!—
    Then, venom, to thy work.   [*Stabs the* KING.
All. Treason! treason!
King. O! yet defend me, friends; I am but hurt.
Hamlet. Here, thou incestuous, murderous, damnéd Dane,
    Drink off this potion; is thy union here?
    Follow my mother.   [KING *dies.*
Laertes.   He is justly serv'd;
    It is a poison temper'd by himself.
    Exchange forgiveness with me, noble Hamlet:
    Mine and my father's death come not upon thee,
    Nor thine on me!   [*Dies.*
Hamlet. Heaven make thee free of it! I follow thee.
    I am dead, Horatio. Wretched queen, adieu!

You that look pale and tremble at this chance,
That are but mutes or audience to this act,
Had I but time—as this fell sergeant, death,
Is strict in his arrest,—O! I could tell you—
But let it be. Horatio, I am dead;
Thou liv'st; report me and my cause aright
To the unsatisfied.
Horatio.   Never believe it;
I am more an antique Roman than a Dane;
Here 's yet some liquor left.
Hamlet.   As thou 'rt a man,
Give me the cup: let go; by heaven, I 'll have 't.
O God! Horatio, what a wounded name,
Things standing thus unknown, shall live behind me.
If thou didst ever hold me in thy heart,
Absent thee from felicity awhile,
And in this harsh world draw thy breath in pain
To tell my story.   [*March afar off, and shot within.*
                    What war-like noise is this?
Osric. Young Fortinbras, with conquest come from Poland,
To the ambassadors of England gives
This war-like volley.
Hamlet.   O! I die, Horatio;
The potent poison quite o'er-crows my spirit:
I cannot live to hear the news from England,
But I do prophesy the election lights
On Fortinbras: he has my dying voice;
So tell him, with the occurrents, more and less,
Which have solicited—The rest is silence.   [*Dies.*
Horatio. Now cracks a noble heart. Good night, sweet prince,
And flights of angels sing thee to thy rest!
Why does the drum come hither?   [*March within.*
          Enter FORTINBRAS, *the English* Ambassadors, *and Others.*
Fortinbras. Where is this sight?
Horatio.   What is it ye would see?
If aught of woe or wonder, cease your search.
Fortinbras. This quarry cries on havoc. O proud death!
What feast is toward in thine eternal cell,
That thou so many princes at a shot
So bloodily hast struck?
First Ambassador.   The sight is dismal;
And our affairs from England come too late:
The ears are senseless that should give us hearing,

　　　To tell him his commandment is fulfill'd,
　　　That Rosencrantz and Guildenstern are dead.
　　　Where should we have our thanks?
Horatio.　　　　　　　　　　　　Not from his mouth,
　　　Had it the ability of life to thank you:
　　　He never gave commandment for their death.
　　　But since, so jump upon this bloody question,
　　　You from the Polack wars, and you from England,
　　　Are here arriv'd, give order that these bodies
　　　High on a stage be placéd to the view;
　　　And let me speak to the yet unknowing world
　　　How these things came about: so shall you hear
　　　Of carnal, bloody, and unnatural acts,
　　　Of accidental judgments, casual slaughters;
　　　Of deaths put on by cunning and forc'd cause,
　　　And, in this upshot, purposes mistook
　　　Fall'n on the inventors' heads; all this can I
　　　Truly deliver.
Fortinbras.　　　　Let us haste to hear it,
　　　And call the noblest to the audience.
　　　For me, with sorrow I embrace my fortune;
　　　I have some rights of memory in this kingdom,
　　　Which now to claim my vantage doth invite me.
Horatio. Of that I shall have also cause to speak,
　　　And from his mouth whose voice will draw on more:
　　　But let this same be presently perform'd,
　　　Even while men's minds are wild, lest more mischance
　　　On plots and errors happen.
Fortinbras.　　　　　　　　　　Let four captains
　　　Bear Hamlet, like a soldier, to the stage;
　　　For he was likely, had he been put on,
　　　To have prov'd most royally: and, for his passage,
　　　The soldiers' music and the rites of war
　　　Speak loudly for him.
　　　Take up the bodies: such a sight as this
　　　Becomes the field, but here shows much amiss.
　　　Go, bid the soldiers shoot.

　　　　　[*A dead march. Exeunt, bearing off the bodies; after which a peal of
　　　　ordnance is shot off.*